ZAGATSURVEY®

2000

ROCKY MOUNTAIN TOP RESTAURANTS

Edited by Bill St. John
and Ann Orton

Coordinated by Andrew Berk
and Kelley Nakamura

Published and distributed by
ZAGAT SURVEY, LLC
4 Columbus Circle
New York, New York 10019
Tel: 212 977 6000
E-mail: zagat@zagatsurvey.com
Web site: www.zagat.com

Acknowledgments

We thank Andrew Berk, Joan Brett, Bill Clarke, Hsiao-Ching Chou, Michael Comstedt, Kerrin Degnan, Rich Grant, Barbara Kimball, Donna Lavery-Lerner, Joyce Meskis, Linda Millemann, Kelley Nakamura, Joe Rassenfoss, Scott Rowitz, Rodney Smith, Penny and Colin St. John and Jan Zeman.

We also thank Russell Orton , Allyson Gygi and the wonderfully innovative chefs of Colorado and Utah who bring joy to our food works.

Contents

Starters

Here are the results of our *2000 Rocky Mountain Top Restaurants Survey* covering nearly 400 establishments in Colorado and Utah.

By regularly surveying large numbers of local restaurant-goers, we think we have achieved a uniquely current and reliable guide. We hope you agree. More than 1,980 people participated. Since the participants dined out an average of 3.1 times per week, this *Survey* is based on nearly 320,000 meals per year.

We want to thank each of our participants. They are a widely diverse group in all respects but one – they are food lovers all. This book is really "theirs."

Of the surveyors, 57% are women, 43% are men; the breakdown by age is 14% in their 20s, 24% in their 30s, 24% in their 40s, 26% in their 50s and 12% in their 60s or above.

To help guide our readers to the best meals and best buys in the Rocky Mountain area, we have prepared a number of lists. See, for example, Colorado's Most Popular Restaurants (page 13), Top Ratings (pages 14–16) and Best Buys (page 17) and Utah's Most Popular Restaurants (page 95), Top Ratings (pages 96–98) and Best Buys (page 99). On the assumption that most people want a quick fix on the places at which they are considering eating, we have tried to be concise and to provide handy indexes.

We are particularly grateful to our editors, Bill St. John, food editor of *The Denver Post*, and Ann Orton, restaurant critic of Salt Lake City's *Deseret News*.

We invite you to be a reviewer in our next *Survey*. To do so, simply send a stamped, self-addressed, business-size envelope to ZAGAT SURVEY, 4 Columbus Circle, New York, NY 10019, or e-mail us at rockymtn@zagat.com, so that we will be able to contact you. Each participant will receive a free copy of the next *Rocky Mountain Top Restaurants Survey* when it is published.

Your comments, suggestions and even criticisms of this *Survey* are also solicited. There is always room for improvement with your help.

New York, New York
April 5, 2000

Nina and Tim Zagat

What's New

In keeping with the spirit of conciseness that characterizes Zagat reviews, we are pleased to announce that this *2000 Rocky Mountain Top Restaurants Survey* is our most compact compilation to date, culling Colorado's and Utah's most important establishments (from the humble to the haute). While we've streamlined the *Survey* so that it's more efficient and user-friendly, this region has been beefing up its dining scene.

Fueled by growth in employment, population and personal income, Colorado restaurant sales grew by 6.3% in 1999, according to the National Restaurant Association. That ranks the Rocky Mountain U.S. Census Region as the first in growth in the entire country – for the fourth time in as many years.

Along the Front Range, the battle for dining dollars continues to pit independents (some dating to the '50s) against an onslaught of chains that increasingly win over families, budget noshers and "eatertainment" groupies (witness the new LoDo hotspot Buca di Beppo).

In the mountain resorts, where the bulk of Colorado's more terrific eateries do their thing, chefs and operators breathe headier air and play riskier games. If money is to be made in Colorado restaurants, it will be where well-heeled skiers and other sports buffs spend their vacations and plenty of green.

But a dry winter (such as in 1999) can be an ouch on the bottom line for even the best-situated mountain restaurant. And more than the weather is fickle: after the hiring hoopla, star toque Keith Luce stayed at The Little Nell for all of three months in early 1999.

That said, the adventurous restaurateur is still a fixture in the hills, with two high-end ventures from high-profile chefs entering the Aspen competition in 1999: Conundrum from George Mahaffey (ex Little Nell) and, in the St. Regis, an Olives branch from Boston empire-builder Todd English.

Denver's eatery action has expanded from LoDo and Cherry Creek to a more scattershot landscape: the hip Rue Cler in Hilltop, the urban bistro Ambrosia along plainspoken East Colfax Avenue, Painted Bench near what was, until it opened, Downtown's Needle Alley and all-the-buzz Beehive in Congress Park. It's great to note that all of these very popular newcomers are home-grown independents, as is Meritage, midway between Denver and Boulder.

Another local favorite, Kevin Taylor's much-loved Zenith, is back on the scene, reopened in the spectacular space of his former Brasserie Z, which wasn't catching on.

Papillon Cafe, this *Colorado Survey*'s big winner (No. 1 for Food and Popularity), has climbed the Denver sky on a savvy combination of pinpoint service partnered with a lengthy menu of French-Asian treats in nearly baroque presentations, the signature of chef-owner Radek Cerny.

And since the last full *Survey,* a plateful of notables closed: in the Denver area, Pacific Star Supper Club, 15 Degrees, 32nd Avenue Grill, La Coupole and Moondance, as well as Carnevale and Shrine Mountain Inn in the mountains.

In Utah, the forthcoming Winter Olympics 2002 are fueling rapid development and an increasingly cosmopolitan flair in the state's restaurant scene. While longtime standbys like the New Yorker Club and Log Haven continue to draw crowds, and another evergreen, Fresco Italian Cafe, captured the No. 1 ranking for Food, new faces introduce a sense of adventure. Downtown's upscale and boutique Hotel Monaco offers the eclectic Bambara, while the laid-back, suburban Rivers Effortless Dining prepares classy, Contemporary American cuisine. Two bare-bones entries, Big City Soup and Em's, share a ramshackle building on the edge of the proposed Gateway development, but count big-time flavors on their luncheon-only menus.

Seems as though ya' gotta be a grill to hang a restaurant shingle in the Salt Lake market. Former Park City guru, Barbara Hill, runs Snake Creek Grill, a Regional American in Heber City. Park City's new Blind Dog Grill features crab cakes the mountain folk inhale, while the skewer-laden servers at Rodizio Grill create a Brazilian carnivore's haven.

The mountain scene witnessed the departure of some perennial favorites – the Greek Hungry i retired its banner, while the Barking Frog's lusty Southwestern flavors succumbed to proposed construction agendas. Ethnic-inspired mainstays, Pomodoro and L'Hermitage, gave way to the economic squeeze, while the tony Il Sansovino felt the pinch of a corporate merger and closed its doors.

We hope you enjoy this *Survey*'s focus on what's best in Rocky Mountain dining (especially since the average cost of a meal at the restaurants contained herein is a rather reasonable $23.48 for Colorado and $28.03 for Utah). We figure you'll run across the pedestrian eateries on your own anyway, so we point you in the direction of those where dining out is still the right place to be.

Denver, Co	Bill St. John
Salt Lake City, UT	Ann Orton
April 5, 2000	

Dining Tips

Over our 20-plus years of surveying restaurant-goers, we've heard from hundreds of thousands of people about their dining-out experiences.

Most of their reports are positive – proof of the ever-growing skill and dedication of the nation's chefs and restaurateurs. But inevitably, we also hear about problems.

Obviously, there are certain basics that everyone has the right to expect when dining out:

1. Courteous, hospitable, informative service

2. Clean, sanitary facilities

3. Fresh, healthful food

4. Timely honoring of reservations

5. Smoke-free seating

Sadly, if these conditions aren't met, many diners simply swallow their disappointment, assuming there's nothing they can do. However, the truth is that diners have far more power than they may realize.

Every restaurateur worth his or her salt wants to satisfy customers, since happy clients equal a successful business. Rather than the adversaries they sometimes seem to be, diners and restaurateurs are natural allies – both want the same outcome, and each can help the other achieve it.

Towards that end, here are a few simple but sometimes forgotten tips that every restaurant-goer should bear in mind:

1) Speak up: If dissatisfied by any aspect of your experience – from the handling of your reservation to the food, service or physical environment – tell the manager. Most problems are easy to resolve at the time they occur – but not if management doesn't know about them until afterward. The opposite is also true: if you're pleased, speak up.

2) Spell out your needs ahead of time: If you have specific dietary requests, wish to bring your own wine, want a smoke-free (or smoking) environment, or have any other special needs, you can avoid disappointment by calling ahead to make sure the restaurant can satisfy you.

3) Do your part: A restaurant's ability to honor reservations, for example, is largely dependent on diners honoring reservations and showing up on time. Make it a point to cancel reservations you're unable to use and be sure to notify the restaurant if you'll be late. The restaurant, in turn, should do its best to seat parties promptly, and, if there are delays, should keep diners informed (a free drink doesn't hurt either).

4) Vote with your dollars: Most people tip 15 to 19%, and often 20% or more at high-end restaurants. Obviously, you have the right not to tip at all if unhappy with the service; but in that case, many simply leave 10% to get the message across. If you like the restaurant, it's worth accompanying the low tip with a word to the management. Of course, the ultimate way to vote with your dollars is not to come back.

5) Put it in writing: Like it or not, all restaurants make mistakes. The best ones distinguish themselves by how well they acknowledge and handle mistakes. If you've expressed your complaints to the restaurant management but haven't gotten a satisfactory response, write to your local restaurant critic, with a copy to the restaurant, detailing the problem. That really gets the restaurateur's attention. Naturally, we also hope you'll express your feelings, pro and con, by voting on zagat.com.

Key to Ratings/Symbols

This sample entry identifies the various types of information contained in your Zagat Survey.

(1) Restaurant Name, Address & Phone Number

(2) Hours & Credit Cards

(3) ZAGAT Surveyor Ratings

F	D	S	C
23	5	9	$19

Tim & Nina's ◑ S ⊅

4 Columbus Circle (8th Ave.), 212-977-6000

■ "What a dump!" – open 7 days a week, 24 hours a day, this successful "deep dive" started the "deli-tapas craze" (i.e., tidbits of pastrami, corned beef, etc. on cracker-size pieces of stale rye); though the place looks like a "none-too-clean garage" and T & N "never heard of credit cards or reservations", "dirt cheap" prices for "great eats" draw demented crowds.

(4) Surveyors' Commentary

The names of restaurants with the highest overall ratings, greatest popularity and importance are printed in **CAPITAL LETTERS**. Address and phone numbers are printed in *italics*.

(2) Hours & Credit Cards

After each restaurant name you will find the following courtesy information:

◑ .... *serving after 11 PM*

S .... *open on Sunday*

⊅ .... *no credit cards accepted*

(3) ZAGAT Surveyor Ratings

Food, **Decor** and **Service** are each rated on a scale of **0** to **30**:

F	D	S	C

F	....	*Food*
D	....	*Decor*
S	....	*Service*
C	....	*Cost*

23	5	9	$19

0 - 9	.... *poor to fair*
10 - 15	.... *fair to good*
16 - 19	.... *good to very good*
20 - 25	.... *very good to excellent*
26 - 30	.... *extraordinary to perfection*

▽ 23	5	9	$19

▽ .... *Low number of votes/less reliable*

The **Cost (C)** column reflects surveyors' estimated price of a dinner with one drink and tip. Lunch usually costs 25% less.

A restaurant listed without ratings is either an important **newcomer** or a popular **write-in**. The estimated cost, with one drink and tip, is indicated by the following symbols.

–	–	–	VE

I	.... *$15 and below*
M	.... *$16 to $30*
E	.... *$31 to $50*
VE	.... *$51 or more*

(4) Surveyors' Commentary

Surveyors' comments are summarized, with literal comments shown in quotation marks. The following symbols indicate whether responses were mixed or uniform.

◪	.... *mixed*
■	.... *uniform*

Colorado's Most Popular

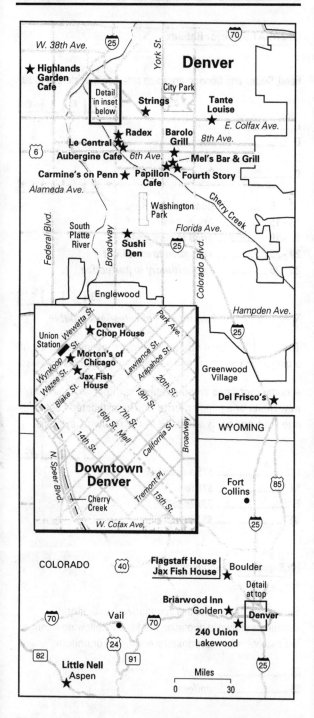

★ Highlands Garden Cafe

(25) W. 38th Ave.
(70)
York St.
Denver
City Park
Strings ★
Tante Louise ★
E. Colfax Ave.
8th Ave.
Radex ★
Barolo Grill
(6) **Le Central** ★
Aubergine Cafe 6th Ave.
Mel's Bar & Grill ★
Carmine's on Penn ★ **Papillon Cafe** ★ **Fourth Story**
Alameda Ave.
Washington Park
Federal Blvd.
Cherry Creek
South Platte River
Florida Ave.
Broadway
Sushi Den ★
(25)
Colorado Blvd.
Englewood
Hampden Ave.

Downtown Denver

Wewatta St.
Park Ave.
Denver Chop House ★
Union Station
Wynkoop St.
Lawrence St.
Arapahoe St.
20th St.
Morton's of Chicago ★
Wazee St.
Jax Fish House
Blake St.
19th St.
16th St. Mall
17th St.
California St.
14th St.
Broadway
N. Speer Blvd.
Tremont Pl.
Cherry Creek
15th St.
W. Cofax Ave.

(25)
Greenwood Village
Del Frisco's ★

WYOMING

Fort Collins ●
(85)

COLORADO
(40)
Flagstaff House
Jax Fish House ★ Boulder
Detail at top
Briarwood Inn
Golden ★
Denver
(70)
Vail ●
(70)
240 Union
Lakewood
(24)
(91)
(82)
Little Nell
Aspen ★
(25)
Miles
0   30

Colorado's Most Popular Restaurants*

Each of our reviewers has been asked to name his or her five favorite restaurants. The 20 spots most frequently named, in order of their popularity, are:

1. Papillon Cafe
2. Barolo Grill
3. Aubergine Cafe
4. Flagstaff House/B
5. Highlands Garden Cafe
6. Tante Louise
7. Fourth Story
8. Strings†
9. Briarwood Inn
10. Denver Chop House
11. Sushi Den
12. Radex
13. Little Nell Restaurant/A
14. Morton's of Chicago
15. Mel's Bar & Grill
16. Carmine's on Penn
17. Le Central
18. 240 Union
19. Jax Fish House
20. Del Frisco's

It's obvious that many of the restaurants on the above list are among the most expensive, but Colorado diners also love a bargain. Were popularity calibrated to price, we suspect that a number of other restaurants would join the above ranks. Thus, we have listed 20 Best Buys on page 17.

---

* All restaurants are in Denver & Environs unless otherwise noted (A=Aspen; B=Boulder & Environs; Br=Breckenridge Area; N=North of Denver; O=Other Mountain Areas; S=South of Denver; V=Vail Area).
† Tied with the restaurant listed directly above it.

Top Ratings*

Top 20 Food Ranking

28 Papillon Cafe
   Highlands Garden Cafe
   Sweet Basil/V
27 Renaissance/A
   Keystone Ranch/Br
   Palace Arms
   Splendido/V
   Sushi Den
   Wildflower/V
   Tante Louise

   Grouse Mtn. Grill/V
   Charles Court/S
   La Petite Maison/S
26 Briarwood Inn
   Alpenglow Stube/Br
   Cafe Brazil
   La Montaña/O
   Barolo Grill
   Piñons/A†
   Del Frisco's

Top Spots by Cuisine

American (New)
28 Highlands Garden Cafe
   Sweet Basil/V
27 Renaissance/A
   Keystone Ranch/Br
   Splendido/V

American (Regional)
27 Grouse Mtn. Grill/V
26 Alpenglow Stube/Br
   Piñons/A
   Cafe Alpine/Br
   Fawn Brook Inn/N

American (Traditional)
27 Palace Arms
26 Briarwood Inn
25 Bang!
   Beano's Cabin/V
24 Assignments

Breakfast/Brunch**
24 Augusta
   Ellyngton's
23 Original Pancake House
22 Watercourse Foods
   Finster Bros.

Chinese
24 Imperial Chinese Seafood
22 Palace Chinese
   Pan Asia Noodle/B
21 La Chine
   Chef's Noodle House

Continental
27 Palace Arms
   Charles Court/S
26 Flagstaff House/B
   Swan at Inverness
   Fawn Brook Inn/N

Delis
25 Parisi
24 Pasta Pasta Pasta
23 Cucina Leone
   Maria's Bakery & Deli
21 New York Deli News

Dessert
24 Alpenrose/V
23 House of Windsor
   janleone
   Andre's Confiserie
22 Jou Jou

French
28 Papillon Cafe
27 Tante Louise
   La Petite Maison/S
   Picasso/V
26 Left Bank/V

French Cafe/Bistro
26 Soupçon/O
   Aubergine Cafe
25 Cafe Bohemia
24 Cache Cache/A
23 Le Delice

---

* Excluding restaurants with low voting; all restaurants are in Denver & Environs unless otherwise noted (A=Aspen; B=Boulder & Environs; Br=Breckenridge Area; N=North of Denver; O=Other Mountain Areas; S=South of Denver; V=Vail Area).
† Tied with the restaurant listed directly above it.
** Other than hotels.

Top Food

Hotel Dining
27 Palace Arms
   Brown Palace
   Charles Court/S
   Broadmoor
26 Little Nell Restaurant/A
   Little Nell Hotel
   Swan at Inverness
   Inverness
25 Penrose Room/S
   Broadmoor

Italian
26 Barolo Grill
   Campagna/O
   Full Moon Grill/B
25 Gabriel's/S
   Cafe Jordano

Japanese
27 Sushi Den
25 Sushi Tora/B
   Takah Sushi/A
   Domo
24 Mori Sushibar

Mediterranean
27 Renaissance/A
26 John's/B
   Aubergine Cafe
   Strings
24 Mel's Bar & Grill

Mexican
26 La Montaña/O
23 Brewery Bar II
   Taqueria Patzcuaro
   El Taco de Mexico
22 La Cueva

Middle Eastern
23 Jerusalem
   Cedars
22 Damascus
   Mataam Fez
   Sahara

Newcomers/Rated
25 Kevin Taylor
   Radex
   Domo

Newcomers/Unrated
   Beehive
   Rue Cler
   Sunflower/B
   Trilogy/B

Offbeat
26 Cafe Brazil
25 India's
   Gasthaus Eichler/O
   Poirrier's Cajun/Br
   Krabloonik/A

Pizza
25 Parisi
   Basil Doc's Pizza
24 Pantaleone's
23 Edgewater Inn
20 Wazee Supper Club

Seafood
26 240 Union
25 Montauk Seafood Grill/V
24 Jax Fish House
   Cherry Crest Market
   McCormick's Fish House

Steakhouses
26 Del Frisco's
   Morton's of Chicago
24 Brook's
   Palm, The
   Ruth's Chris

Thai
25 J's Noodles
24 Busara
23 Tommy's Oriental
   Wild Ginger
22 Sawaddee/B

Vietnamese
25 New Saigon
24 New Orient
23 Rose's Cafe
   Thai Hiep
22 T-Wa Terrace

Western
24 Fort, The
   Denver Chop House
23 Emil-Lene's
22 Table Mtn. Inn
21 Buckhorn Exchange

Top 20 Decor Ranking

28 Alpenglow Stube/Br
Palace Arms
Domo
Beano's Cabin/V
27 Wildflower/V
Flagstaff House/B
Charles Court/S
Splendido/V*
Keystone Ranch/Br
Briarwood Inn

Fort, The
Highlands Garden Cafe
Penrose Room/S
Manor House
26 Fawn Brook Inn/N
Wellshire Inn
Tante Louise
Kevin Taylor
Grouse Mtn. Grill/V
Little Nell Restaurant/A

Outdoor

Ajax Tavern/A
Highlands Garden Cafe
Little Nell Restaurant/A
Maria's Bakery & Deli

Potager
Strings
Sushi Tazu
Sweet Basil/V

Romantic

Aubergine Cafe
Cafe Bohemia
Cafe Paradiso
Fawn Brook Inn/N
Highlands Garden Cafe

Kevin Taylor
Manor House
Palace Arms
Penrose Room/S
Tante Louise

Rooms

Domo
Flagstaff House/B
Kevin Taylor
Palace Arms
Piñons/A

Renaissance/A
Ship Tavern
Vesta Dipping Grill
Wildflower/V
Zenith

Views

Ajax Tavern/A
Alpenglow Stube/Br
Chart House
Flagstaff House/B

Hearthstone/Br
Krabloonik/A
Manor House
Penrose Room/S

Top 20 Service Ranking

27 Keystone Ranch/Br
Palace Arms
La Petite Maison/S
26 Fawn Brook Inn/N
Briarwood Inn
Tante Louise
Penrose Room/S
Highlands Garden Cafe
Little Nell Restaurant/A
Alpenglow Stube/Br

Charles Court/S
Renaissance/A
Splendido/V
Piñons/A
Swan at Inverness
25 Ellyngton's
Flagstaff House/B
Wildflower/V
Soupçon/O
Papillon Cafe

---

* Tied with the restaurant listed directly above it.

www.zagat.com

Best Buys

20 Top Bangs For The Buck

This list reflects the best dining values in our *Survey.* It is produced by dividing the cost of a meal into the combined ratings for food, decor and service.

1. Finster Bros.
2. Maria's Bakery & Deli
3. Davies Chuck Wagon Diner
4. Parisi
5. House of Windsor
6. Dot's Diner/B
7. Hot Cakes
8. Original Pancake House
9. Butterhorn Bakery & Cafe/Br
10. Chez Jose
11. Jalapeño Mexican Grill
12. Egg-Ception Eatery
13. El Taco de Mexico
14. Swing Thai
15. Market, The
16. Dumitri's
17. Brewery Bar II
18. Andre's Confiserie Suisse
19. El Tejado
20. Watercourse Foods

Alphabetical Directory of Colorado Restaurants

Denver & Environs

TOP 3 FOOD RANKING

Restaurant	Cuisine Type
28 Papillon Cafe	New French
Highlands Garden Cafe	New American
27 Palace Arms	American/Continental

F	D	S	C

Ambrosia
–	–	–	M

5410 E. Colfax Ave. (Grape St.), Denver, 303-388-8429
Take a used-up East Denver cafe, add a talented chef, a good scouring and some color, and you have this hip New American with Asian touches; eats ranging from lamb dumplings over a tomato relish to BBQ veal chop are bolstered by a smart little wine list and decent service.

Andre's Confiserie Suisse
23	19	21	$14

370 S. Garfield St. (bet. Alameda & Dakota Aves.), Denver, 303-322-8871
☑ You need not be a "blue-haired lady", but it helps at this Cherry Creek Swiss-Continental/bakery serving "two good choices" daily and pastry "perfection"; some prefer the bakery, but it's a "ladies' lunch spot par excellence."

Annie's Cafe ⑤
18	15	18	$11

4012 E. Eighth Ave. (east of Colorado Blvd.), Denver, 303-355-8197
■ A wild mix of "scrub suits from the neighboring hospital", "crazy" "'50s" relics on the walls, mounds of "retro" "home cooking" and jars of "peanut butter on the tables" distinguishes this "unpretentious" East Denver diner prized for its "old-fashioned" breakfasts, shakes and burgers.

Assignments
24	20	23	$25

School of Culinary Arts, 675 S. Broadway (bet. Center & Exposition Aves.), Denver, 303-778-6625
☑ Run by "hardworking" culinary students, this South Central American-Continental earns high grades for its "impeccable food and service"; it may be "inconsistent", but they "succeed more often than not."

AUBERGINE CAFE ⑤
26	22	24	$30

225 E. Seventh Ave. (bet. Grant & Sherman Sts.), Denver, 303-832-4778
■ For "true Mediterranean bistro food" in what some call the "most romantic setting in the city", fans head to this near-Downtown "friendly, comfortable and consistent" "little slice of heaven" with "innovative" cooking, a "carefully selected wine list" and a "knowledgeable staff"; but this "like-Provence" "gem" can be "a little crowded", so reserve early.

Augusta 🇸   24 | 25 | 23 | $38 |

*Westin Hotel, 1672 Lawrence St. (bet. 16th & 17th Sts.),
Denver, 303-572-7222*

◪ The enormous windows offer "great views" of Downtown
Denver at this "beautiful" Traditional American lauded for
its "attention to every detail" and "elegance all the way"; but
many loyalists lament that this former dinner "favorite"
now serves breakfast only – "too bad; it was wonderful."

Avenue Grill 🇸   21 | 20 | 20 | $23 |

630 E. 17th Ave. (Washington St.), Denver, 303-861-2820

■ The "bartenders know martinis" and the kitchen knows
"great burgers", fish and pasta say regulars of this "old
standby", a "cosmopolitan" Uptown American that's
"heaven for cigar smokers" with a "great bar scene" –
just be prepared for "dinner with the accent on 'din'."

Bang!   25 | 14 | 17 | $14 |

*3609 W. 32nd Ave. (bet. Lowell Blvd. & Meade St.), Denver,
303-455-1117*

■ A "tiny", "bang-up", North Denver "hole-in-the-wall"
serving "superb" "homestyle" American food ("wonderful
soups", "great meat loaf") that's "exactly what mom should
have cooked but couldn't"; despite "counter service",
"fluorescent lighting" and the "competition to snag a table",
addicts yearn for a "clone" in their nabe – though many
also yearn for a liquor license.

Banzai   22 | 15 | 18 | $21 |

*6655 Leetsdale Dr. (1 block east of Monaco Pkwy.), Denver,
303-329-3366*

■ Lauded as an "excellent alternative" to other sushi shops,
this "creative" East Denver Japanese is prized for its
"friendly staff", "big selection" and "huge slabs of fish"; the
"cafeteria atmosphere" may be plainspoken, but it's a
"jewel" nonetheless – "all the sushi chefs in town go here."

BAROLO GRILL   26 | 25 | 24 | $37 |

*3030 E. Sixth Ave. (bet. Milwaukee & St. Paul Sts.), Denver,
303-393-1040*

■ "Go to Italy or go here" rave fans of the "scrumptious"
cooking at this "lovely" East Denver Northern Italian, where
the "owner's attention to details shows", especially in the
"best Italian wine list in the West"; although service, while
"knowledgeable", strikes critics as "self-important", ratings
support boosters who say it "gets better every year."

Basil Doc's Pizza 🇸🥡   25 | 12 | 19 | $13 |

*2107 E. Virginia Ave. (bet Gaylord & Vine Sts.), Denver,
303-778-7747*

■ "Hands down" "the best pizza in Colorado" boast boosters
of this Washington Park pie palace turning out "tasty",
"made-to-order" pizzas with "fantastic" "East-Coast"
"crispy crusts"; but it's "takeout only" and no delivery.

Beehive – | – | – | M |
606 Corona St. (E. 6th Ave.), Denver, 303-832-5766
A new addition to the Congress Park neighborhood, this hip Med–New American combines the winning duo of Janice Henning (chef) and hubby Tim Elenteny (sommelier) for terrific, hearty eats and super (mostly imported) wines.

Bistro Adde Brewster 23 | 20 | 22 | $27 |
250 Steele St. (bet. 2nd & 3rd Aves.), Denver, 303-388-1900
■ If "consistent" and "affordable" food (including the "best burger in town") doesn't lure you to this Cherry Creek American-French bistro, then perhaps its "cosmopolitan atmosphere", "great late-night scene" and "friendly servers" will; it's also a "favorite" for ladies who lunch, though some issue warnings about "snobbish" regulars.

Bonnie Brae Tavern S 19 | 12 | 17 | $13 |
740 S. University Blvd. (bet. Exposition & Ohio Aves.), Denver, 303-777-2262
◪ The "super" 'za at this south of Cherry Creek local pizzeria "isn't the only reason to go" claim loyal regulars who also love the "funky" "'60s decor" ("aqua vinyl seat covers") and steak specials; but "tons of atmosphere" isn't enough to placate critics who gripe about "smoke, hustle" and "crowds" and claim that even the pizza is "not all that."

Bourbon Street Pizzabar & Grill 20 | 18 | 18 | $16 |
5117 S. Yosemite St. (Belleview Ave.), Greenwood Village, 303-721-6150
■ Pie pals flock to this New Orleans–accented Greenwood Village spot for its "world tour of pizza", featuring a "huge selection" of "imaginative" "designer" pies bolstered by "good" side salads and homemade desserts; it's "family-owned" and family-friendly, too – a relief when the rug rats are in tow.

Breakfast Inn S 18 | 9 | 19 | $10 |
6135 E. Evans Ave. (bet. Holly St. & Monaco Pkwy.), Denver, 303-757-7491
■ Ok, so this East Denver hash house is "plain" (even "ugly"), and the smoking section's fog spills over to the whole house; but it's still a "great place" for "inexpensive", "outstanding breakfasts" (omelets, huevos rancheros and breakfast burritos) and you can count on "really fast service"; N.B. 20% off from 3–5 PM, Monday–Friday.

Brewery Bar II 23 | 12 | 20 | $12 |
150 Kalamath St. (bet. 1st & 2nd Aves.), Denver, 303-893-0971
■ They should hand out water buckets at the door of this Mexican just south of Downtown Denver, where heat-seekers congregate for "awesome", "hot, hot" "green chile to clear the sinuses" and the "best crispy chile rellenos in town"; it may be "seedy" and "smoky", but "come early or you'll be waiting" in line.

BRIARWOOD INN, THE 🅂   26 27 26 $40
1630 Eighth St. (Hwy. 58 & US 6), Golden, 303-279-3121
☑ "Don't eat the day before you dine here" advise patrons of this "lavish", "romantic" American-Continental in Golden known for "superb multicourse meals" in an atmosphere of "absolute elegance" that's "perfect for a special occasion"; though a few bicker it's "past its prime", it remains a "traditionalist's paradise" that's "expensive and worth it."

Brook's Steak House & Cellar   24 24 23 $47
6538 S. Yosemite Circle (north of Arapahoe Ave.,
off Yosemite St.), Greenwood Village, 303-770-1177
☑ "Fantastic if someone else is paying" is how meat lovers sum up this "elegant" Denver steakhouse that's "perfect for special occasions" with service provided by "pros"; though a few growl about "average food at top dollar" and fault "close tables", most rate it among the "best in town" – but "thank goodness for expense accounts."

Brothers Barbeque 🅂   – – – I
6499 Leetsdale Dr. (Monaco St.), Denver, 303-399-9329
Some say the "best BBQ in Denver" comes from these two "guys from England", twentysomething sibs turning out "saucy, lip-smacking ribs and chicken and great sides too"; it's "all prepared with care and flavor", but in the great 'cue tradition, the "place looks like a dump" so "takeout is best."

Bruno's Italian Bistro 🅂   22 18 21 $24
Villa Monaco Shopping Ctr., 2223 S. Monaco Pkwy.
(Evans Ave.), Denver, 303-757-4500
☑ Penne pinchers love this "moderately priced" Italian, a "delightful surprise in a strip mall" with "simple food done right", an "affordable wine list", "hospitable service" and a "very willing-to-please" owner; dissenters judge it just "ok", but they're outvoted by enthusiasts who add "May is to die for" – "it's calamari month."

Buca di Beppo 🅂   – – – M
1400 Market St. (14th St.), Denver, 303-595-3287
Wild and wacky, this LoDo outpost of the national chain offers a tried-and-true formula: mammoth portions of fair fare (all Italian-style), cooled Chianti in *fiaschi,* and so many pictures, papal blessings and Geppetto-like figurines that the place fairly screams Epcot Eyetalian.

Buckhorn Exchange 🅂   21 24 20 $33
1000 Osage St. (10th Ave.), Denver, 303-534-9505
☑ Meat lovers moo contentedly over this "real West" Downtown steakhouse filled with "great history" (it holds "Colorado Liquor License No. 1") as well as hundreds of "animal heads on the wall" so "you can watch what you eat and have it watch you back"; although "an overrated tourist trap" to many, some find it "surprisingly good", even if "prices are too high."

Budapest Bistro
23 | 20 | 22 | $24

1585 S. Pearl St. (Iowa Ave.), Denver, 303-744-2520
■ This "traditional" Hungarian "delight" near Washington
Park draws warm applause for its "cozy, charming decor",
"excellent", "authentic" cooking that's "never overseasoned
or heavy" and "caring" owners who "treat you like
regulars"; it may be a "little cramped", but that equals
"intimate and romantic" to smitten enthusiasts.

Burnsley Hotel Dining Room, The ⑤
22 | 23 | 22 | $30

Burnsley Hotel, 1000 Grant St. (10th Ave.), Denver, 303-830-1000
☑ Admirers say the main dining room of this all-suites hotel
just south of Downtown is an "elegant", "quiet" and
"charming hideaway" offering "classic" Continental
"dining like it used to be"; although a few find the food
"inconsistent", more agree it's "carefully prepared and
presented", and "convenient covered parking" is a plus.

Busara ⑤
24 | 18 | 18 | $23

1435 Market St. (bet. 14th & 15th Sts.), Denver, 303-893-2884
☑ The votes are in on this new Thai, and it comes up a
"great addition to LoDo" earning plaudits for "fresh and
creative" food at "reasonable" prices; while it's still a "gem
in the rough" that gets "loud and crowded" (especially at
lunch), with a staff that's "friendly" but "on a learning curve",
all is forgiven – it's "yummy Thai without going to the 'burbs."

Cafe Berlin ⑤
23 | 16 | 21 | $22

2005 E. 17th Ave. (bet. Race & Vine Sts.), Denver, 303-377-5896
■ "Solid" City Park Berliner known for "perfectly prepared"
"homestyle" food that's "as good as German gets", served in
a "cozy space" that's "enlivened with vibrant art"; it's "the
real thing", although the "friendly staff" is sometimes "slow."

Cafe Bohemia
25 | 16 | 19 | $27

*1729 E. Evans Ave. (bet. Gilpin & Williams Sts.), Denver,
303-777-7222*
☑ "They have a vision" applaud devotees of this "creative,
cheery" Central Denver French-American bistro, a "special
secret" with a "perfectionist chef-owner" turning out
"stylish" fare that's "not generic"; but what's a "cozy space"
to some elicits groans over "hole-in-the-wall discomfort"
from others, and service gets "overburdened" when busy.

Cafe Brazil ⊘
26 | 17 | 23 | $25

3611 Navajo St. (W. 36th Ave.), Denver, 303-480-1877
■ The "smells will drive you crazy and make your tongue
dance" gush admirers of the "fabulous food" you will
"dream about and crave" at North Denver's "hip" Brazilian
"hideaway"; it may be just a "hole-in-the-wall with
style", but it's "homey", service is "charming" and oh, the
grub – an "indescribable, wonderful melding of flavors";
N.B. reservations are "a must" – and so is hard cash.

Cafe del Sol ⑤
18 | 14 | 19 | $12

608 Garrison St. (6th Ave.), Lakewood, 303-238-7999
■ If it's "quantity" for "cheap" that you're after, this Lakewood Greek-Mexican delivers with "solid family fare" from two distinctly different but equally sunny climes (the Mexican menu sports "heart-stopping sauces"); it's "an excellent neighborhood cafe" with "friendly" servers, and as for decor, check out the "cute birdhouses."

Cafe Evangeline
19 | 16 | 18 | $19

30 S. Broadway (bet. Archer Pl. & Ellsworth Ave.), Denver, 303-282-8955
☑ Those ragin' for Cajun in South Central Denver fill up at this "cramped", "noisy" South Broadway yearling that's gaining a rep for the "authentic flavors of New Orleans"; most agree it's a "good value", even though quality ranges from "excellent to fair" and the staff "needs training."

Cafe Jordano
25 | 15 | 21 | $18

11068 W. Jewell Ave. (S. Kipling Pkwy.), Lakewood, 303-988-6863
■ "Why can't everywhere be like this little gem?" wonder admirers of this "very friendly" Lakewood "mom-and-pop" Italian, a "small", "homey" place with "authentic", "classic" cooking (by "natives") "that you'll savor for days"; it's widely considered a "best value", so "get there when the doors open" or "plan to wait for a table."

Cafe Paprika
22 | 14 | 19 | $16

13160 E. Mississippi Ave. (Uvalda St.), Aurora, 303-755-4150
☑ "Authentic Middle Eastern food", including "tasty" Moroccan specialties like "exquisite chicken b'steeya", earns nods as a "good value" at this "down-home" Aurora spot; but while some diners praise the "friendly" chef-owner whose "presence makes service exceptional", others moan that he "wants continuous reassurance"; your call.

Cafe Paradiso
23 | 19 | 22 | $28

2355 E. Third Ave. (Josephine St.), Denver, 303-321-2066
■ A "nice alternative to trendy Cherry Creek" eateries, this "adorable" Eclectic-Mediterranean is paradise indeed, thanks to its "delightful owners", "civilized", "romantic atmosphere" (like "a private dining room") and "excellent food"; a few still standing at the gates grouse "the menu never changes and gets boring."

California Cafe Bar & Grill ⑤
24 | 24 | 22 | $28

Park Meadows Mall, 8505 Park Meadows Ctr. Dr., upper level (bet. County Line Rd. & I-25), Littleton, 303-649-1111
■ It's in a shopping mall, but that doesn't hinder devotees of the "innovative menu", "fantastic wine selection", "attentive staff", "beautiful decor" and "great atmosphere" at this "upscale, trendy" Park Meadows Californian; faultfinders sniff "big plate, little food, big price", but they're outvoted.

Canino's Trattoria   24 | 20 | 22 | $24
2390 S. Downing St. (bet. Evans & Yale Sts.), Denver,
303-778-1994
☑ Admirers say the "gracious owners" of this South Central
Denver Italian have an "underrated gem" (but "please
stop discovering it!") that serves "genuine", "yummy" food
(including "homemade bread") that's "the best in the area";
a minority shrugs it's just "middle-of-the-road", but scores
indicate that the "spectacular soups" and "perfect pastas"
win the day.

Carmine's on Penn ⑤   24 | 19 | 20 | $25
92 S. Pennsylvania St. (Bayaud Ave.), Denver,
303-777-6443
☑ "Known for huge family-size dishes", this "very noisy"
Southern Italian import from NYC draws "huge crowds"
("reservations are a must") to its south of Downtown locale;
although the food is "super most times, bland others", and
service ranges from "well-trained" to "arrogant beyond
belief", the "garlic knots rule" and the "excellent affordable
wine list" is another big plus; bottom line: "go with a group"
and go hungry.

Cedars   23 | 17 | 22 | $20
1550 S. Federal Blvd. (Florida Ave.), Denver,
303-936-2980
■ "What a treasure!" is the consensus about this South
Denver Middle Eastern and its "delicious" (mostly)
Lebanese fare; it may have a "so-so location" and "little
decor", but the "nice owners" who "always make you
feel welcome" operate a "clean, neat" house with a
"family atmosphere" and "consistently excellent food."

Central 1   22 | 14 | 19 | $18
300 S. Pearl St. (Alameda Ave.), Denver, 303-778-6675
■ Try the "combination plates if you can't decide on one
thing" at South Central Denver's "most authentic Greek";
it's "our hero" say saganaki lovers who award gold medals
for the "excellent dishes and huge portions" served in a
"very cute" Hellenic atmosphere.

Chart House ⑤   22 | 23 | 22 | $35
25908 Genesee Trail Rd. (I-70, exit Genesee Park), Golden,
303-526-9813
☑ "A great view but a '50s mentality" sums up the mixed
feelings of many diners concerning the Genesee outpost
of this national seafooder-steakhouse chain; while it's
"dependable" for "very good steaks" and a "huge salad
bar", there are gripes aplenty about "ho-hum" food that's
"overpriced"; still, some who "get a window seat" "at
dusk" find it a fine "spot to celebrate."

Cheesecake Factory ☒   20 | 19 | 18 | $21
The Shops at the Tabor Ctr., 1201 16th St. (Larimer St.), Denver, 303-595-0333

☒ "Go very hungry and leave very full" from this Downtown Eclectic, where hordes line up for "excellent cheesecake" and "way too big portions" of most anything cookable; although foes complain that the "gross portions" are of "ordinary" quality ("factory says it all"), fans are sold on the "good value, consistency" and "high-energy atmosphere" – "if this is a factory I want to move to an industrial area."

Chef's Noodle House ☒☒   21 | 8 | 17 | $10
10400 E. Sixth Ave. (1 block west of Havana St.), Aurora, 303-363-6888

■ "You don't need ambiance" insist devotees of this "very plain" Aurora Asian (in a former Taco Bell) where the "quick", "cheap", "plentiful" and "terrific" eats are "close to perfect"; all agree it's "the best of fast food" and just right for a "noodle fix."

Cherry Crest Market ☒   24 | 12 | 19 | $22
Cherry Crest Ctr., 5909 S. University Blvd. (Orchard Ave.), Littleton, 303-798-2600

■ A wholesale fishmonger doubling as a restaurant, this "reasonably priced" Littleton seafood house with "echoes of the East Coast" may be the "best in town" according to fans of its "always fresh" and "very tasty" fin and gill; but "don't come for the atmosphere" (there's "none at all") – "just good food."

Cherry Cricket ☽☒   20 | 12 | 17 | $13
2641 E. Second Ave. (bet. Clayton & Columbine Sts., opp. Cherry Creek Mall), Denver, 303-322-7666

■ There's "no better burger anywhere" insist partisans of this "dive" institution in Cherry Creek, a burger barn also much loved for its fiery green chile, "classic" "homemade soups" and "great draft beer selection" (more than 20); former gripes about "overwhelming smoke" should blow over with the installation of a pricey new ventilation system.

Cherry Tomato ☒   – | – | – | M
4645 E. 23rd Ave. (Dexter St.), Denver, 303-377-1914

While this Park Hill "neighborhood" Italian was inadvertently left off the *Survey*, many loyal fans wrote in to praise its "reasonably priced", "unpretentious", "family-style" cooking and terrific wines; set in an old mosaic-floored drugstore, it's a favorite for families who make it "their joint on Sunday nights"; N.B. no reservations but call ahead to be put on the waiting list.

Chez Jose ⑤
21 | 13 | 16 | $10

3027 E. Second Ave. (St. Paul St.), Denver, 303-322-9160
■ The "big-as-your-head burritos" with "fresh-grilled" meat and fish fillings rate "five estrellas" from adherents of this Cherry Creek Mexican; a new bar area and a "larger dining room" also win favor, along with the self-serve salsa bar; but "good luck finding a parking spot."

Chez Michelle ⑤
21 | 20 | 21 | $27

1515 Madison St. (Colfax Ave.), Denver, 303-321-3311
☑ Little sister to Normandy French Restaurant next door, this East Denver Gallic is a "comfortable" and "cheaper" alternative, with a "gracious owner" offering what some call the "best French food for the money in the metro area", including "a bargain $15 prix fixe"; although critics say it "never seems to make it" and call for an "update", defenders swear it's a place for "great food without snottiness."

Chez Thuy Hoa
22 | 12 | 16 | $16

1500 California St. (15th St.), Denver, 303-623-4809
Thuy Hoa ⑤
28080 Douglas Park Rd. (Main St.), Evergreen, 303-674-5421
■ A "standout" duo serving some of the "best" Vietnamese in town; despite the Downtown locale's "schlocky decor and noisy crowds", it's still prized as a "good, cheap lunch spot" with "fabulous" food, and Evergreen sports the same menu – and Hoa herself.

Chez Walter
23 | 19 | 22 | $29

5969 S. University Blvd. (Orchard Rd.), Littleton, 303-794-4026
■ Fanciers of this "cozy", "romantic" "little secret" in Littleton bask in its "rich, delicious" Continental-Swiss and other "European bistro cooking" (don't miss the rösti potatoes) in a "Swiss lodge atmosphere"; while it's just a "neighborhood place", it's a "real fave" and "it'll cost you."

Chinook Tavern
22 | 22 | 19 | $28

265 Detroit St. (bet. 2nd & 3rd Aves.), Denver, 303-394-0044
☑ Owned by an architect and artist, this International in Cherry Creek earns kudos for its "beautiful interior and patio" as well as its "wonderful" German specialties ("superb spaetzle", "outstanding schnitzel"), "good service" and "great selection of beer"; dissenters carp over the "noisy bar" and find "nothing outstanding" except the "attitude", but they're outvoted.

Chipotle Mexican Grill ⑤
20 | 15 | 16 | $9

5545 Wadsworth Bypass (W. 55th Ave.), Arvada, 303-431-6963
12131-D E. Iliff Ave. (east of Peoria St.), Aurora, 303-873-1300
1205 S. Havana St. (Mississippi Ave.), Aurora, 303-369-3700
3600 W. 32nd Ave. (Lowell Blvd.), Denver, 303-964-3323
745 Colorado Blvd. (8th Ave.), Denver, 303-333-2121

Chipotle Mexican Grill (Cont.)
333 E. Alameda Ave. (bet. Grant & Logan Sts.), Denver,
303-733-1331
1644 E. Evans Ave. (Gilpin St.), Denver, 303-722-4121
Tamarac Sq., 7350 E. Hampden Ave. (1½ blocks east of
Yosemite St.), Denver, 303-741-8980
1300 Pennsylvania St. (E. 13th Ave.), Denver, 303-831-8831
1600 California St. (16th St.), Denver, 303-615-5818
8647-A E. Arapahoe Rd. (Yosemite St.), Greenwood Village,
303-488-2002
220 Union Blvd. (bet. 2nd & 3rd Aves.), Lakewood, 303-716-0707
Park Meadows Shopping Ctr., 8331 S. Willow St.
(County Line Rd.), Littleton, 303-768-0102
7541 S. University Blvd. (Dry Creek Rd.), Littleton, 303-797-7001
3294-A Youngfield St. (32nd Ave.), Wheat Ridge, 303-234-1600
☑ Colorado's best-known (and largest homegrown) fast-food
chain is a "gourmet" Mexican proffering "good, wholesome
and quick" "made-to-order burritos huge enough for two" in
"modern, simple" surroundings; but plenty of naysayers tout
other jumburitto joints and "don't get the hype" over this one.

Coos Bay Bistro   22 | 17 | 19 | $24
2076 S. University Blvd. (Evans Ave.), Denver, 303-744-3591
☑ Cheek by jowl to the University of Denver is this "friendly"
New American "neighborhood hangout" that delights with
an "upscale menu for a decent price" featuring "fresh
ingredients imaginatively prepared"; the "intimate dining
room" is "like eating at a friend's", though it can get "noisy."

Cucina Leone 🖥   23 | 20 | 19 | $23
763 S. University Blvd. (bet. Exposition & Ohio Aves.),
Denver, 303-722-5466
☑ "An interesting mix of takeout and dine-in" marks this
Italian-Mediterranean near Cherry Creek; while it's a "great
place to assemble a picnic", "intimate dinners" are possible,
too, and Denver's "best rotisserie chicken" works either
way; some say "service needs refining", but the generally
"excellent quality" brings them back.

Damascus 🖥   22 | 12 | 17 | $15
2276 S. Colorado Blvd. (Iliff Ave.), Denver, 303-757-3515
■ The "best hummus", "amazing pita bread" and "great
kebabs" are just a few of the reasons many call this "tiny"
South Central Denver Middle Eastern "the best in town";
"reasonable prices" and "large portions" don't hurt either.

Davies Chuck Wagon Diner 🖥⇘   17 | 21 | 19 | $9
9495 W. Colfax Ave. (Hoyt St.), Lakewood, 303-237-5252
☑ Lakewood's "original greasy spoon" isn't really "retro,
it's just unchanged" – "an aluminum, one-piece" railroad
diner with "good value" eats ("where else can you get
$3.99 steak-and-eggs?") and "great" waitresses who sling
more than blue plates; though a few sniff it "stinks of cigs",
nostalgists say it's "worth it for the atmosphere."

Dazzle Restaurant & Lounge   23 19 21 $27
930 Lincoln St. (bet. 9th & 10th Aves.), Denver,
303-839-5100
☑ It does, say most about this "hip" New American near
Downtown with "great martinis", "terrific crab cakes"
and "excellent service" in a "sleek" setting ("the exterior
is deceptive"); "it doesn't", maintain an outvoted few who
find the decor "cold" and the kitchen "uneven"; but with
"something for every price point", it's worth a try.

Del Frisco's Double Eagle   26 25 25 $48
Steak House
Denver Tech Ctr., 8100 E. Orchard Rd. (I-25),
Greenwood Village, 303-796-0100
■ "Texas comes to Denver" at this "extremely expensive
but excellent" Greenwood Villager, where a "top-notch"
staff delivers "power dinners" of "great" martinis and
mammoth hunks of seared steer in a "clubby setting"
accented by a "fabulous cigar bar"; though many find it
"incredibly enjoyable" (and rate it the top steakhouse in
the *Colorado Survey*), a few beef "big is not always
beautiful" and warn you'll "spend a bundle."

Denver Buffalo Company S   20 21 19 $31
1109 Lincoln St. (11th Ave.), Denver, 303-832-0880
☑ What's most favored at this near-downtown Regional
American steakhouse/bar/deli/trading post/nightclub/art
gallery is hard to say, but this "Colorado original" is
definitely "impressive for out-of-towners"; there's plenty
of "hearty" game and buffalo (bison) on the plates, but
tightwads growl "Native Americans wouldn't have eaten
it at these prices."

DENVER CHOP HOUSE S   24 22 21 $30
1735 19th St. (Wynkoop St.), Denver, 303-296-0800
☑ Set in a former railroad shed cheek by jowl to Coors
Field in LoDo, Colorado's busiest restaurant is a "noisy",
"yuppie city" Regional American steakhouse that gets the
green light from most for its "lively" atmosphere and "huge
servings" of "excellent" food, but is derailed by a few as
"too much of a scene" ("ritzy-titzy crowds", "pretentious"
staff); "reservations are a must" and bring a pen – it's a
hit with "sports teams."

DOMO   25 28 21 $23
1365 Osage St. (Colfax Ave.), Denver, 303-595-3666
■ "A joy to the palate and a delight to the eyes" gush
devotees of this "unique" Downtowner that's "like a
Japanese country inn" with a "very traditional menu" ("no
sushi, no sashimi") of "food you didn't even know existed";
but the "stunning" decor ("stone tables", "large Japanese
garden") and unusual, "authentic" fare draw crowds,
leading to "interminable waits" (no reserving), and "inept"
service doesn't help matters.

Dora's Mexican Restaurant   15 | 15 | 17 | $12 |
*2406 S. Parker Rd. (bet. Havana St. & Iliff Ave.), Aurora,
303-368-1527*
☑ "Decent, inexpensive Mexican food" is the ticket at
this Aurora beanery known for "good enchiladas" and
"great" green chile, with "service so fast, it's like it's
psychic"; there's "lots of food for a low price", but also
lots of grumbles: "an atmosphere like a barn", "there's
better Mexican out there."

Dozens 🆂   20 | 16 | 19 | $12 |
2180 S. Havana St. (Warren Ave.), Aurora, 303-337-6627
236 W. 13th Ave. (Bannock St.), Denver, 303-572-0066
☑ These "cheerful", "charming" and "consistently good"
breakfast specialists earn dozens of compliments for "large
portions" of "creative, healthy and cleverly named" morning
fare bolstered by "strong Bloody Marys"; a "great staff"
and "quick" "quality" lunches draw more applause, but at
2 PM these "tiny" outlets close up shop, so don't come
looking for dinner.

Duffy's Shamrock ●🆂   15 | 13 | 18 | $12 |
1635 Court Pl. (bet. Broadway & 17th St.), Denver, 303-534-4935
■ Combine a "75-foot-long bar", "basic, cheap and fast"
"home cooking" and an, um, interesting Downtown "big
city" crowd, and you have this "Irish to the core" hash
house and bar; it may be "dark" and "smoky", but it's also
"unpretentious" and "straightforward" – "in-out-full."

Dumitri's 🆂   19 | 15 | 20 | $12 |
*Havana Sq. Shopping Ctr., 1911 S. Havana St. (Jewell Ave.),
Aurora, 303-752-0553*
■ For "inexpensive" "home cooking", especially "great
breakfasts" and a "good brunch" on weekends, surveyors
make a beeline to this "well-run, sparkling clean" Aurora
Greek diner that's family-run and staffed with "cheerful
servers who enjoy children."

Edgewater Inn ●🆂   23 | 13 | 17 | $13 |
5302 W. 25th Ave. (Sheridan Blvd.), Edgewater, 303-237-3524
■ Surveyors routinely rave over the "thin-crust" "pizza
perfecto" at this Edgewater "institution" and pie palace
near Sloans Lake that's been a "family-run", "venerable
neighborhood watering hole" for ages; sure, "the floor
smells like beer" (who's sniffing around down there?), but
the pizza's "the best."

Egg-Ception Eatery 🆂   20 | 16 | 19 | $12 |
2790 S. Havana St. (Yale Ave.), Aurora, 303-755-9839
■ It's "basic" and "down-home", but this Aurora AM
specialist delivers "exactly what you walked in for": a "nice
variety" of "very good breakfasts" ("fabulous blueberry
pecan waffles") that are a "good value" and brought to
table by "friendly" staffers; N.B. lunch is also served.

Eggshell & Incredibles Cafe S | 19 | 15 | 18 | $11 |
1520 Blake St. (bet. 15th & 16th Sts.), Denver,
303-623-7555
■ "A hangover's best friend" advise tipplers who favor
this Cherry Creek breakfast (and lunch) bistro with a
"neighborhood feel", "excellent breakfasts, great menu
selection and fast service"; Sunday brunch is "tops", but
"you can read an entire newspaper while waiting for a
table" so "get there early" – those who don't say it's
"worth the wait."

El Azteca | 21 | 11 | 16 | $12 |
3960 S. Federal Blvd. (bet. Hampden & Oxford Aves.),
Sheridan, 303-761-3639
El Azteca Grill and Cantina
Aurora Highlands Shopping Ctr., 1780 S. Buckley Rd.
(bet. Iliff & Mexico Aves.), Aurora, 303-755-2735
■ Looking for "rotisserie chicken without peer"? – then
vamos to this Mexican duo (with Cuban accents) for
singular birds and other "great" south-of-the-border fare,
served "very fast" and in "big portions" at a "good price."

Ellyngton's S | 24 | 25 | 25 | $36 |
Brown Palace Hotel, 321 17th St. (bet. Broadway &
Tremont Pl.), Denver, 303-297-3111
■ You might spot "Denver's mayor" at this Downtown
Traditional American (the second dining room of The Brown
Palace Hotel), because it's all about "power" munches at
this "meeting place for the city's professional and business
people"; despite high ratings, a few say "the food is good
but ordinary", but service is "outstanding" and all agree it
puts out "the best Sunday brunch: lavish, pricey and over
the top"; N.B. no dinner.

El Taco de Mexico S⊅ | 23 | 8 | 13 | $9 |
714 Santa Fe Dr. (7th Ave.), Denver,
303-623-3926
■ Most agree this Santa Fe Drive taco shack has the "most
authentic Mexican food in Denver" – including "absolutely
the best chile relleno on the planet" and the "primogenitor of
all breakfast burritos" – cooked by capable mamacitas
amid "decor that borders on the hilarious"; in sum: "great
food, really cheap."

El Tejado S | 22 | 13 | 18 | $11 |
2651 S. Broadway (Yale Ave.), Denver, 303-722-3987
■ From its "broad menu" of "wonderful food", this South
Central Denver Mexican serves the "best chicken burritos in
town", "excellent chile rellenos" and "good margs"; it's
"always a treat" and "reasonably priced", although many
"could do without" the "loud, intrusive" mariachi music.

Emil-Lene's Sirloin House S   23 | 14 | 21 | $28 |
16000 Smith Rd. (east of Chambers Rd.), Aurora, 303-366-6674
■ You'll think you've driven to Kansas when you get to this way away, "funky", "old-fashioned" steakhouse in Aurora, but there are rewards: "a straightforward menu" of "huge", "superbly cooked" steaks "served with spaghetti" on the side; "out-of-towners love it" and the longtime waitresses (nary a waiter) are "pros"; decor? – well, a "tree grows through the middle of the dining room."

Empress Dim Sum Restaurant S   20 | 14 | 16 | $18 |
2825 W. Alameda Ave. (1 block east of Federal Blvd.), Denver, 303-922-2822
■ No need to wait for weekends to enjoy "great" dim sum at this South Central Denver Chinese – it's served "all day, every day"; or opt for "Denver's best dining value: a $12.95 live lobster" dinner in an "elaborately decorated", "spacious room" that's sometimes "noisy" "with catering events" ("Cambodian weddings") that make it "especially fun."

Ethiopian Restaurant S⊅   21 | 11 | 17 | $17 |
2816 E. Colfax Ave. (bet. Detroit & Fillmore Sts.), Denver, 303-322-5939
■ Even though there's "no atmosphere" and the menu is "small" at this East Denver Ethiopian, most agree it's a "fine ethnic experience" with "unbelievably good food" "served in an authentic fashion"; the "friendly" "owner remembers every customer for years."

Falafel King   18 | 10 | 14 | $9 |
Republic Plaza, 303 16th St. (bet. Court & Tremont Pls.), Denver, 303-573-7203
Tabor Ctr., 1201 16th St. (bet. Larimer & Lawrence Sts.), Denver, 303-629-6603
825 Colorado Blvd. (bet. 8th & 9th Sts.), Denver, 303-322-6077 S
■ Why eat a fast-food burger when you can have "better" "quick" eats that are "healthy and interesting" at this "bargain" "eat-and-run" Middle Eastern minichain?; fans call it "perfect at what it does", although a few partisans of other falafel flingers insist "it's no king."

Finster Bros. Bagel **Bakery & Cafe** S   22 | 16 | 18 | $8 |
630 E. Sixth Ave. (Washington St.), Denver, 303-777-6060
5709 E. Colfax Ave. (Ivy St.), Denver, 303-377-2088
■ Do the "great escape from the big bagel chains" and schmear here, at this "friendly, homey" pair of Denver bagelries making "bagels the way bagels should be" along with "a mean cup of java", "incredible coffee cake" and super sandwiches (though they're "slow to be made" – in a crunch, "the help needs help").

FORT, THE S
24 | 27 | 24 | $41

19192 Hwy. 8 (Hwy. 285), Morrison, 303-697-4771

☑ It may be a "major tourist mecca", but for "adventurous eating in a fun environment", it's tough to beat this "unique" Regional American–cum–"theme park" in a reconstructed adobe fort trading post just outside Denver; for most, it's a "fantastic" "occasion destination" that "stirs up a love of history" with its "old West" decor, "unbeatable views" and menu of buffalo and "great wild game", and if a few gripe about "prices and attitudes as high as the altitude", all agree you "must go once."

FOURTH STORY
RESTAURANT & BAR S
24 | 25 | 23 | $30

Tattered Cover Bookstore, 2955 E. First Ave. (Milwaukee St.), Denver, 303-322-1824

☑ It's books, nooks and cooks at this "charming", "cozy", "classy" Regional American atop Cherry Creek's famed Tattered Cover Bookstore, a "great for dates" spot where the "nicest servers in Denver" bring "fine", "innovative" fare to table; while some close the covers on "slow" service and "too, too loud" live jazz (though it's only at Sunday brunch and Monday dinner), most find it a "consistent pleasure."

Fresh Fish Company S
21 | 19 | 19 | $28

Tiffany Plaza, 7800 E. Hampden Ave. (Tamarac Dr.), Denver, 303-740-9556

☑ Although one school swears this Southeast Denver fish house serves the "best seafood" "tasting fresh off the dock" and "one of the best Sunday brunches around", skeptics maintain its fin fare comes "fresh out of the frozen food section" in "landlocked Colorado" and that "reasonable prices seem as lost as Atlantis"; take the dive? – buoyant ratings bolster supporters.

Gallery Cafe S
24 | 21 | 20 | $30

The Marketplace, 1193 Bergen Pkwy. (south of Evergreen Pkwy.), Evergreen, 303-674-5967

☑ Some may find it a "bit pricey for the area", but most are pleased to have a "really special place" in Evergreen with a "dress-up atmosphere", "good" New American food that's "getting better" from an "expanded menu", a "rotating art gallery" and jazz on Tuesdays and Thursdays; uneven service ("untrained" but "friendly") may need a little work, but the "efforts are evident" and locals are happy.

Gandhi India's Cuisine S
20 | 16 | 18 | $20

5071-B S. Syracuse St. (Belleview Ave.), Denver, 303-694-7388

■ The "most complete Indian menu in Denver" (from tandoori to vegan) is found at this Greenwood Village curry cafe according to acolytes who pay special homage to its "reasonably priced" lunch buffet that's "unmatched in quality and variety"; "friendly service" adds more appeal, although a few insist that "there's better Indian in town."

Golden Europe S   23 | 17 | 22 | $16
Shops at Wadsworth, 6620 Wadsworth Blvd. (bet. 66th & 67th Aves.), Arvada, 303-425-1246
☑ You "can't get anything but a good meal" at this well-priced, "not fancy but comfortable" Arvada German-Czech according to fans who "beg for their fruit dumplings" or "to-die-for roast duck"; the "nice folks" and "solid", "artery-clogging" eats make it "enjoyable" for most – just bring your appetite and "leave your calorie counter at home."

Healthy Habits S   19 | 12 | 13 | $11
Belcaro Shopping Ctr., 865 S. Colorado Blvd.
(bet. Kentucky & Ohio Aves.), Denver, 303-733-2105
Denver West Village, 14195 W. Colfax Ave. (I-70, exit 263), Golden, 303-377-9293
7418 S. University Blvd. (Dry Creek Rd.), Littleton, 303-740-7044
☑ "Healthy" is up to you – those short on "self-control" "like the unhealthy dessert section" – at the "wholesome", "huge", "fresh" and "tasty buffets" laid out by this salad/soup/pasta/pizza minichain; it's "an amazing value", although faultfinders gripe that it's just a "cafeteria" for "gluttons" and it "takes an act of Congress to get dishes removed."

HIGHLANDS GARDEN CAFE   28 | 27 | 26 | $33
3927 W. 32nd Ave. (bet. Osceola & Perry Sts.), Denver, 303-458-5920
■ "Open your eyes, it's not a dream" counsel enthusiasts of this North Denver New American (No. 2 for Food in the *Colorado Survey),* where two "lovely older homes" redone into softly lit dining rooms provide the setting for "one of Denver's very best" and well-priced menus; "if you eat inside, though, you've missed" the "fabulous gardens", so "dine by candlelight among the roses" at what may be the "most romantic restaurant in town."

Hot Cakes Breakfast & Lunch S   20 | 14 | 19 | $10
1400 E. 18th Ave. (Humboldt), Denver, 303-830-1909
■ Up and at 'em for "everything you could want in a breakfast spot" at this "pleasant" Uptown diner known for "huge servings" of "elaborate" morning eats ("lunch is great, too") and "efficient service"; it's "good if you're spending time" at Denver's nearby hospitals, though fans "wish they were stacked in more than one location"; no dinner.

House of Windsor   23 | 23 | 23 | $12
1050 S. Wadsworth Blvd. (Mississippi Ave.), Lakewood, 303-936-9029
■ A bit of Olde England dropped from the sky one day and became this "charming" Lakewood teahouse that's "perfect for Anglophiles" for "a very proper" "afternoon tea and scones" or "the best meat pies" and other light lunch fare; just "don't expect a full meal."

Hugh's New American Bistro   25 | 23 | 22 | $29
1469 S. Pearl St. (bet. Arkansas & Florida Aves.), Denver,
303-744-1940

✓ "Exquisite, wholesome" "innovative" food "sure to please carnivores and vegetarians alike" earns garlands of praise for this "beautiful" Washington Park New American, a "romantic dinner place in a quiet area of town"; though a few feel both "service and food slipped" in the past year, ratings support those who call it a "gem" – don't miss the "most amazing ladies' room in town (a flower bower)."

Il Fornaio 🔄   21 | 24 | 20 | $28
1637 Wazee St. (bet. 16th & 17th Sts.), Denver,
303-573-5050

✓ "It's hard to believe it's a chain" insist pasta watchers who pronounce this LoDo Italian "outstanding" for its "fantastic" breads (take some home from the on-site bakery), "beautiful space" and "great" regional cooking; but phobes pan "too much formula": "just ok" food, "variable service" and "noise."

Imperial Chinese Seafood   24 | 22 | 22 | $22
Restaurant 🔄
431 S. Broadway (Dakota Ave.), Denver, 303-698-2800
■ Once again the No. 1 Chinese restaurant in the *Survey* (and "deservedly so"), this South of Downtown routine winner is "still the best" according to legions of loyalists who laud its "elegant" ambiance, "excellent" food and professional service in a "quiet setting" where you can "dine rather than eat"; a few rebels swear it's "overrated", but they're soundly outvoted.

India's 🔄   25 | 20 | 20 | $23
Tamarac Sq., 3333 S. Tamarac Dr. (Hampden Ave.),
Denver, 303-755-4284
✓ Lots of raj-rajs celebrate this "upscale" Southeast Denver Indian's "excellent" food, "killer lunch buffet" and "nice decor", and "it's a good thing the food is so good" because the cheering fades away over "weak" service that varies from "attentive" to "slow" and "scornful"; still, when you crave a curry fix, many dub it "best in town."

Jalapeño Mexican Grill 🔄   19 | 10 | 14 | $9
5701 Leetsdale Dr. (bet. Holly & Jersey Sts.), Denver,
303-333-5305
■ Ya gotta go for the "fab" fish tacos at this quickie, "fresh and inexpensive" Southeast Denver Mexican seafooder that's "relatively health oriented" but always "friendly and fast"; the "ambiance is mediocre", but some "could eat there every day", starting with the "huge breakfast burritos."

janleone S | 23 | 24 | 22 | $29 |
1509 Marion St. (Colfax Ave.), Denver, 303-863-8433

✉ Jan earns stellar reviews for her "creative menu" of Continental-Italian goodies and "great desserts" (from daughter Mara) cooked up in the kitchen of a "lovely, warm and romantic" renovated East Colfax "mansion"; devotees dub it a "secret treasure" that's especially nice on a "cold, snowy night", although variable service ("excellent" vs. "unfriendly") can be a hazard.

Japon S | 23 | 19 | 20 | $25 |
1028 S. Gaylord St. (Mississippi Ave.), Denver, 303-744-0330

■ Banzais all around for this Washington Park Japanese serving "first-rate" sushi and other "high-quality" fare in a "modern", "stylish" setting; the "fabulous deals at happy hour" are another draw, but best of all, for many, is that it's a "less pretentious alternative" to rival Sushi Den nearby.

Jax Fish House S | 24 | 19 | 20 | $27 |
1539 17th St. (Wazee St.), Denver, 303-292-5767

✉ The praise – and pans – come in waves for this "hip" Denver seafooder (with a Boulder branch) offering "proof that you can get great seafood without a nearby coast"; although the "fresh fish" is "perfectly prepared" and the "bustling atmosphere" strikes some as "vibrant" and "fun", others rail about the "deafening music", "rude yuppie crowds" and "no reservation" policy; your call.

Jerusalem Restaurant ◑S | 23 | 9 | 14 | $12 |
1890 E. Evans Ave. (bet. Broadway & University Blvd.), Denver, 303-777-8828

✉ Falafel fanciers dig the "dirt cheap but very tasty" eats at this Middle Eastern near the University of Denver; it's the "best food for the least money" and "terrific for vegetarians", so even if it is a "dump", keep it in mind "for takeout."

Johnny's Diner S⊅ | 15 | 13 | 15 | $10 |
2323 S. Havana St. (Iliff Ave.), Aurora, 303-369-8307

■ The "best grease fix this side of a gas station" draws those in need to this "friendly, quick" Aurora diner for its "large portions" of "no-nonsense" chow and "diner-grade cups of joe"; the place "could be cleaner" but, hey, dat's part of da charm; N.B. breakfast and lunch only.

Jou Jou S | 22 | 22 | 21 | $30 |
Hotel Teatro, 1106 14th St. (Arapahoe St.), Denver, 303-228-0770

✉ For "flavorful", "creative food in a cool space" that's "convenient to the theater complex", many head to Kevin Taylor's Downtown American-French bistro (those without tickets may want to snag "mezzanine seating for great entertainment" of the people-watching variety); despite flaws – "tables too tiny for a martini", "uncertain service", "small, pricey portions" – it's "highly recommended" before a show.

J's Noodles 🅂 ≠ 25 | 10 | 20 | $13
945 S. Federal Blvd. (bet. Ford Pl. & Kentucky Ave.),
Denver, 303-922-5495
◪ It may be "the Woolworth's of Thai" in a "very tiny,
crowded", "no-frills" space where you must "go early or
stand in line", yet legions love to Thai one on at this South
Central Denver "heaven in a strip mall"; "cooked by a
grandma from Bangkok", its "kick-ass" green papaya salad
and banana leaf soup "never fail to please."

Kevin Taylor 25 | 26 | 25 | $54
Hotel Teatro, 1106 14th St. (Arapahoe St.), Denver, 303-820-2600
◪ Although star chef Kevin Taylor's Downtown New
American scores highly, diners report mixed reactions:
aficionados point to the "elegant" food, "ethereal" space,
"amazing wine list" and "superb ingredients", but foes
retort it's "too expensive for us to bear the growing pains"
("my wallet hurts just thinking about it") and claim its "reach
exceeds its grasp"; ratings, however, side with fans.

Kim Ba 22 | 14 | 18 | $14
2495 S. Havana St. (bet. Iliff Ave. & Parker Rd.), Aurora,
303-745-1637
■ Out Aurora way, you'll find this "small", unpretentious
Vietnamese that's "consistently at the top of its form"
serving "great food with fresh ingredients" in a "pleasant
atmosphere"; main drawback: sometimes slow service.

La Chine 🅂 21 | 21 | 20 | $23
5071-A S. Syracuse St. (bet. Belleview & Union Aves.),
Denver, 303-220-8885
◪ Most chopstickers salute this establishment as "the best
Chinese in South Metro", citing its "excellent food and
service" in a "beautiful", "upscale" setting with "flowers
on the table"; although a few cleavers take aim at "bland",
"overrated" cooking, they're a minority.

La Cueva 22 | 16 | 19 | $15
9742 E. Colfax Ave. (Dayton St.), Aurora, 303-367-1422
◪ For "fresh", "authentic", "consistent" eats ("killer
margs", homemade tortillas) amid "bright, festive decor",
swing by this "friendly" Aurora Mexican that's "worth the
trip"; a few vocal chile chompers grouse "it's been coasting
for some time", but most still find it a "solid standby."

Las Brisas 🅂 21 | 18 | 19 | $22
6787 S. Clinton St. (1 block south of Arapahoe Rd.),
Englewood, 303-792-3212
◪ Whether it's "Tex-Mex", "Southwestern", "South
American" or "Spanish" matters little to the masses who
say olé to this reasonably priced Englewood beanery's
"unusual" and "stylish" eats ("outstanding guacamole");
it "all tastes great after" the "best margs in town", even if
a few plain old "Mexican" heat-seekers think "it's bland."

L'Auberge Zen ⑤

24 | 19 | 21 | $24

9955 E. Hampden Ave. (bet. Dayton & Florence Sts.), Denver, 303-751-3571

■ "Great for couples" who can't make up their menu minds, this Denver French-Japanese serves "some of the best sushi" in the area as well as "steak au poivre with a side of maguro" in a "somewhat romantic", "white-tablecloth" atmosphere with "consistently good service"; "it feels like you've been on a vacation" – but to which continent?

Le Central ⑤

22 | 20 | 21 | $23

112 E. Eighth Ave. (Lincoln St.), Denver, 303-863-8094

■ "They put the muscle in mussel" at this very popular Downtown Denver French bistro (now with a new chef de cuisine) known for "food and wine a Frenchman cherishes and an American can afford"; even if a few find the cooking "inconsistent" and "not what it used to be", the "French country" ambiance is "charming", and the "great wine list is one of the best values in Denver"; N.B. the daily lunch menu is available on the Internet (www.lecentral.com).

Le Delice

23 | 17 | 17 | $20

250 Steele St. (bet. 2nd & 3rd Aves.), Denver, 303-331-0972

■ Voilà, "a true French experience" say patrons of this Cherry Creek bistro/bakery, where the authenticity extends from the "wonderful" "real French-style bread", "superb soups" (including "great onion soup") and "fabulous desserts" right down to the "arrogant" personnel; despite the "attitude", it offers "simple but enjoyable" dining.

Little Ollie's ⑤

– | – | – | M

2364 E. Third Ave. (Josephine St.), Denver, 303-316-8888

"You'll always find a crowd" at this Cherry Creek Chinese (with a sibling in Aspen), and while it was not originally included in the *Survey*, it seems the whole crowd wrote in to praise its "beautifully presented", "fresh" and "creative Pan-Asian menu" served by an "accommodating" staff; "they do a good job delivering quickly" too.

Little Saigon

23 | 17 | 19 | $20

201 Steele St. (2nd Ave.), Denver, 303-333-4569

■ Combine the "hidden location" of this "underappreciated" Cherry Creek Vietnamese with its "intimate, romantic" ambiance and you have an "oasis from noise" and the chance for a "tasty" and "elegant dinner"; one enthusiast claims "I've been to Saigon – this place has better food."

Long Binh ⑤

▽ 21 | 12 | 18 | $15

940 S. Federal Blvd. (bet. Ford Pl. & Kentucky Ave.), Denver, 303-935-4141

☑ Those with a craving for Vietnamese "goat dishes" and other "good", "steady" SE Asian fare should beeline to this "friendly" South Denver spot; the place is "short on atmosphere", but it's "run by a lovely family."

Luke's, A Steak Place S
22 | 12 | 18 | $29

Independence Sq., 4990 Kipling St. (W. 50th Ave.),
Wheat Ridge, 303-422-3300

☑ "If you just want a good steak at a good price", mosey on over to this Wheat Ridge meatery for "outstanding" slabs of seared steer; though "there's no atmosphere", and by local standards it can get "pricey", this "neighborhood" beef palace merits a stop.

M & D Cafe ⊘
24 | 10 | 17 | $13

2004 E. 28th Ave. (Race St.), Denver, 303-296-1760

■ "Believe the waitress when she describes the sauces" at this "family-run" North Denver barbecue shack, 'cause "the real hot" one "will burn your lips off"; but what's underneath it is "tantalizing and succulent", the "best ribs in town"; leave room for "real homemade sweet-potato pie."

MANOR HOUSE S
22 | 27 | 22 | $33

1 Manor House Rd. (Ken Caryl Rd.), Littleton, 303-973-8064

☑ Take a "lovely old" mansion boasting a "terrific view" overlooking the Ken-Caryl Valley, and appoint it so that you "step back in time", and you have this Continental "house on a hill" in Littleton; though views of the cooking range from "excellent" to "average" and service can be uneven ("good" vs. "disinterested"), ratings side with loyalists who find it "romantic", "especially at Christmas."

Maria's Bakery and Deli ⊘
23 | 16 | 14 | $9

3705 Shoshone Ave. (W. 37th Ave.), Denver, 303-477-3372

■ Northwest Denver has a lot of restaurants, but nothing like this "funky" complex, where the cooking is done in a carriage house and you eat in either a greenhouse or house in winter, and as a "special treat in summer", outdoors on the yard-sale-stuffed "cool patio"; it's "always a big hit" with "can't miss sandwiches" on homemade bread and the "best dessert choices in the city"; N.B. lunch only.

Market, The S
20 | 18 | 14 | $11

Larimer Sq., 1445 Larimer St. (bet. 14th & 15th Sts.),
Denver, 303-534-5140

☑ If you miss the Big Apple, check out this "gourmet", "trendy" LoDo deli/bakery/espresso bar/market where "you order from the counter"; it's a "hip place for lattes" and "people-watching" – "if you like a lot of attitude."

Mataam Fez S
22 | 24 | 23 | $29

4609 E. Colfax Ave. (Cherry St.), Denver, 303-399-9282

■ "Close your eyes and smell the wonderful fragrance of Morocco" at this "unique" "special-occasion treat", an East Denver North African (with branches in Boulder and Colorado Springs) where you "sit on the floor" and dine on the "best lamb" and "finger food at its finest"; it's "not for the belly-phobic, arthritic or fastidious", but for an "exotic" experience, it's "sure to stimulate conversation."

McCormick's Fish House ⑤ | 24 | 22 | 21 | $28 |
*Oxford Hotel, 1659 Wazee St. (17th St.), Denver,
303-825-1107*

☑ Set in the corner of a "historic Downtown hotel" with
an "exquisite, old-world interior", this "dependable" LoDo
seafooder "knows fish"; it sports a "nice wine list" and
offers "lots of great fresh oysters" along with two daily
values: "$1.95 happy hour" small plates in the "classy",
"dark wood" bar, and entrees between 5–6 PM that "cost
the time on the clock."

Mel's Bar & Grill ⑤ | 24 | 22 | 22 | $33 |
*235 Fillmore St. (bet. 2nd & 3rd Aves.), Denver,
303-333-3979*

☑ "Melvyn Master is an excellent host" at his Cherry
Creek North Cal-Med, where the ambiance is "terrific" if
"always slightly chaotic" (especially with the "singles
scene" at the "smoky bar"); add a "frequently changing
menu", "great wine list" and "hip" and "very loyal clientele"
and you've got a "constant in Denver"; those who don't "feel
part of the sophisticated family" gripe that this "Elaine's
wanna-be" is "overrated."

Mercury Cafe ●⑤⧷ | 18 | 18 | 16 | $16 |
2199 California St. (22nd Ave.), Denver, 303-294-9258

■ The menus of activities and food are equally long at
this "fun", "funky" and "friendly" Eclectic-Vegetarian just
north of Downtown; whether you're seeking "great eats
after a swing dance lesson", "live dinner music", a place
to "play pool" or tofu that "tastes gourmet", this "old hippie
hangout" has it – amid "decor that's like a thrift store."

Mori Sushibar & Tokyo Cuisine | 24 | 13 | 18 | $26 |
2019 Market St. (20th St.), Denver, 303-298-1864

■ "Don't let the looks of the place scare you" away from
this plainspoken LoDo Japanese in the "back room" of a
veterans' lodge, since the "great, great sushi" and other
"very good Japanese fare" served here earn consistently
high ratings; a few say it's "not as good as it used to be"
but most insist it's still a "sure bet" and "lunch combos
are a good deal."

Morton's of Chicago ⑤ | 26 | 24 | 25 | $49 |
*1710 Wynkoop St. (17th St., opp. Union Station), Denver,
303-825-3353*

☑ "Meat and martini madness" rules in this kingdom of
excess, a "great Chicago import" that many feel is "still
the best of the steakhouses" with service that's "like a
Broadway show", "big slabs" of "excellent" beef and
prices so high you may feel "like you're eating $5 bills";
although foes growl it's a "stale relic" that "needs a kick
in the pants", it's a clear "favorite" – "all great successes
in business or sports are celebrated here."

My Brother's Bar ◐ | 21 | 18 | 19 | $13 |
2376 15th St. (Platte St.), Denver, 303-455-9991
■ "When you just have to have a burger" with juices "that drip off the elbows", everyone advocates this "funky" "Denver legend" near LoDo; with "no TVs", a "great, friendly staff", only "classical music" from the speakers and a terrific "summer patio", there's "nowhere else like it."

New Orient ⑤ | 24 | 19 | 19 | $18 |
10203 E. Iliff Ave. (bet. Havana St. & Parker Rd.), Aurora, 303-751-1288
■ For "excellent" "New Wave" Vietnamese, including "unusual entrees not found elsewhere", check out this "simply decorated" "class act hidden in a strip mall" in Aurora; "sophisticated seafood" dishes are menu standouts, but don't pass on "wonderful noodle bowls" and "great desserts"; admirers say it "never disappoints."

New Saigon ⑤ | 25 | 14 | 19 | $17 |
630 S. Federal Blvd. (bet. Center & Exposition Aves.), Denver, 303-936-4954
■ "Best", "best", "best" beats the drum for this South Denver Vietnamese where the "outstanding" food from an "encyclopedia of a menu" (40 pages) and the "five-star service" seem even better at "one-[star] prices"; fans of the "complex, high quality" curries and "great noodle bowls" plead "it's full now – don't list it."

New York Deli News, The ⑤ | 21 | 13 | 19 | $14 |
7105 E. Hampden Ave. (½ mi. east of I-25), Denver, 303-759-4741
■ Ok, "it's not NY", but "it's as close as we can get" say aficionoshers of "Colorado's own Carnegie" Deli in Southeast Denver and its combination of "huge portions" ("sandwiches piled a mile high"), "characters" for patrons and "wise-cracking staff"; "don't go if you're easily offended" is less a warning than a recommendation.

Normandy French Restaurant ⑤ | 23 | 23 | 23 | $35 |
1515 Madison St. (Colfax Ave.), Denver, 303-321-3311
◪ For "formal, classic French" dining, *allez vite* to East Denver and this "cozy" old house, a "longtime favorite" where the "old-fashioned, European setting" is "very '50s" and matches the "established" menu and "stately" ambiance; but despite solid scores, most diners think both "menu and decor need updating" and suggest the "hovering" owner provides an "overkill on friendliness."

Original Pancake House, The ⑤ | 23 | 16 | 19 | $11 |
5900 S. University Blvd. (Orchard Rd.), Littleton, 303-795-0573
■ Well, the *original* Original is elsewhere, but this Littleton link in the pancake chain is "always packed" with crowds hungry for "good, good, good" breakfasts of corned beef hash, "feather-light" flapjacks and "huge omelets" brought to table by a "friendly staff."

Pagliacci's S $\qquad$ 21 | 19 | 20 | $21 |
1440 W. 33rd Ave. (Navajo St.), Denver, 303-458-0530

◪ North Denver's "oldest Italian" draws bravos for the "world's best" minestrone served in piping hot tureens before each "hugely portioned" meal; the "dark", "old-world" decor makes it "a romantic favorite", and the "truly traditional meals" are "sure to impress", with only a few tightwads grumbling about "pasta at steak prices."

Painted Bench $\qquad$ ▽ 24 | 17 | 23 | $20 |
400 E. 20th Ave. (Logan St.), Denver, 303-863-7473

◼ This "notable" New American newcomer just outside Downtown rehabbed a century-old building into a "funky, cozy" "grand lunch spot" that's also turning out "excellent" dinners from a revolving menu strong on entree salads and atypical meats and fish; impressed respondents report "no decor" but "close to perfect" service.

PALACE ARMS S $\qquad$ 27 | 28 | 27 | $47 |
Brown Palace Hotel, 321 17th St. (bet. Broadway & Tremont Pl.), Denver, 303-297-3111

◼ The top-drawer dining room of the 104-year-old Brown Palace Hotel ("lots of history"), this Downtown Denver American-Continental is the "only superelegant, plush restaurant left", according to devotees who rave about its "old Denver" "class, class, class", "turn-of-the-century furnishings" and "impeccable" (if slightly "snooty") service; it may be "for the filthy rich", but it's "worth the price" to "feel like royalty"; N.B. jacket and tie required.

Palace Chinese Restaurant S $\qquad$ 22 | 19 | 20 | $19 |
6265 E. Evans Ave. (Monaco Pkwy.), Denver, 303-782-0300

◼ Although a few compare this Southeast Denver Imperial Chinese "sister" to a "cavernous" "barn", it's "beautifully" appointed, and serves "good food for the price."

Palm, The S $\qquad$ 24 | 22 | 23 | $42 |
Westin Hotel, 1201 16th St. (Arapahoe St.), Denver, 303-825-7256

◪ "For that special night when you feel like eating a side of beef" or for a glimpse of "power lunch headquarters", book a table at this "top-notch" Downtown meat mecca where the "no nonsense" "great staff and management" handle the "glitterati" with aplomb; sure, portions are "ridiculous" (with prices to match), but for those who like that sort of dining, "it actually lives up to the hype."

Palomino S $\qquad$ 23 | 25 | 21 | $30 |
1515 Arapahoe St. (16th St.), Denver, 303-534-7800

◪ Those in search of "very good" "gourmet food on a yuppie budget" should gallop over to this "chic, groovy" Cal-Med in Downtown's most "stunning", "fabulous" space; fanciers whinny it's good for "pre- or post-theater", although bolters find it "a little noisy" and ask "does the phrase 'tragically hip' need a poster child?"

Pantaleone's NY Pizza   24 13 19 $15
Holly Plaza, 2120 S. Holly St. (Evans Ave.), Denver, 303-757-3456
■ "Denver's best pizza" runs like a refrain through comments about this Southeast Denver pie palace and its "amazing", "thick-crust" 'za, "oozing with flavor" and using "quality toppings"; it also rolls "the best Sicilian-style at this altitude" – so what if the joint has "zero" decor?

PAPILLON CAFE S   28 25 25 $38
250 Josephine St. (bet. 2nd & 3rd Aves.), Denver, 303-333-7166
■ No. 1 for Food and Popularity in our *Colorado Survey*, this Cherry Creek New French with Asian influences offers chef-owner Radek Cerny's "outstanding" cuisine that's "as beautifully presented as it is delicious" (though wags warn you "could get vertigo" from the vertical constructions); "well-coached servers" and an "intelligent" wine list leave little room for complaint, though one diner tries: "I hate restaurants where everything on the menu is great."

Parisi, An Italian Market & Deli ▽ 25 17 23 $11
4408 Lowell Blvd. (44th St.), Denver, 303-561-0234
■ The "smell alone is worth the trip" to this Italian deli in North Denver serving "authentic [thin-crust] pizza", "excellent pastas" and "great sandwiches"; it's "real" – and no surprise that most of the staff is Italian.

Pasquini's Broadway S   _ _ _ I
1310 S. Broadway (Louisiana Ave.), Denver, 303-744-0917
Pasquini's Uptown S
1336 E. 17th Ave. (Humboldt St.), Denver, 303-863-8252
They're giving it away at these red-sauce Italians, popular for "free garlic knots" and a special list of "$10 bottles of wine"; the "cheap" vino, "good food" and "large portions" work well with the "colorful decor" and "casual" feel, and outdoor dining at both locations is a plus.

Pasta Pasta Pasta   24 12 15 $14
278 Fillmore St. (3rd St.), Denver, 303-377-2782
◪ A "who's who passes through" this "small" eat-in/take-out East Denver Italian deli where the "good stuff" "ain't cheap" but it is "top-notch"; critics gripe about "skimpy portions", "big prices" and occasional "surly" service, but for most, the "amazing" quality compensates; N.B. seated service at lunch only – expect "difficult" parking.

Pete's Kitchen S   19 11 17 $10
1962 E. Colfax Ave. (Race St.), Denver, 303-321-3139
■ If it's a fat fix you need, this "landmark" East Colfax diner has "more grease than Pat Riley's hair"; "pay no attention to the clientele" that lands here "after a wild night" "to sober up" on "the best 2 AM breakfast in town", but do notice the "efficient", "old-school", "wisecracking" service; it may be a "dump", but it's a fab dump, so "get there by 1:30 AM to avoid the line."

Potager   25 | 22 | 22 | $31
1109 Ogden St. (bet. 11th & 12th Aves.), Denver, 303-832-5788
☑ Most agree that this "airy", "hip, urban" New American "addition to the Capitol Hill scene" does up a "clever menu" of "fab food in a funky" but "comfortable" setting (a former laundry in a war zone re-do) where the "outdoor seating in the back is a great touch"; "inconsistent" service is the main complaint, though even fans admit the "adventurous", "changing" bill of fare is "sometimes too avant-garde."

Queen of Sheeba S⊅   ▽ 25 | 10 | 20 | $13
7225 E. Colfax Ave. (Quebec St.), Denver, 303-399-9442
■ Both "a gem and a hole-in-the-wall", this "tiny" East Denver Ethiopian has a fervent following for its "incredible", "superb food", "large portions", "warm atmosphere" and "gracious hosts"; although decor is at a minimum, it's "like visiting a friend's home" – "what fun!"

Radex ●S   25 | 23 | 23 | $29
100 E. Ninth Ave. (Lincoln St.), Denver, 303-861-7999
☑ "Wonderful martinis" and "interesting food" from "genius" chef-owner Radek Cerny conspire to make this less expensive Papillon sib "the best newcomer to Denver", according to its "beautiful people" clientele who rave this New American is "so, so cool, from the hip staff to the superchic interior" – though cynics claim the latter is "like unfinished South Beach"; N.B. live jazz is another draw, although it makes the "upbeat" setting even more "noisy."

Rialto Cafe S   21 | 22 | 20 | $27
934 16th St. (bet. Champa & Curtis Sts.), Denver, 303-893-2233
■ Downtowners enjoy this Mediterranean–New American on the 16th Street Mall for many things: the "sophisticated", "attractive room", "romantic" atmosphere, "nice, small patio" and "inventive dishes" that work well for both a "hip business lunch" and for the "pre- and post-theater crowd"; though some "try to get balcony seats", others think it's "more like an attic" up there.

Richard Lee's Noodle House S   ▽ 18 | 10 | 22 | $12
472 S. Federal Blvd. (Virginia St.), Denver, 303-937-2946
■ Although still "undiscovered", this South Denver Asian turns out "great soups and noodles" in "authentic and delicious" dishes ranging from Chinese to Vietnamese and more; "fluorescent lighting" may be a drawback, but prices are "reasonable" and the atmosphere is "friendly."

Rosa Linda Mexican Cafe S   21 | 11 | 20 | $12
2005 W. 33rd Ave. (Tejon St.), Denver, 303-455-0608
■ The picture is rosy at this "charming" "family-owned" Northwest Denver Mexican, a "neighborhood" "hole-in-the-wall" "known to locals" for its "good food"; it's "not fancy", but it is "authentic."

Rose's Cafe §   23 | 11 | 19 | $20
731 Quebec St. (bet. 7th & 8th Aves.), Denver, 303-377-7649
✉ Unique to Denver, this "neighborhood" East Sider offers Italian, American and Vietnamese dishes and manages to carry off all three cuisines, turning out "insanely huge portions" of "cheap and tasty" eats; "don't be deterred" by the "tacky" decor, but do be prepared for the strong presence of the "very friendly" proprietor.

Rue Cler §   – | – | – | M
5575 E. Third Ave. (Holly St.), Denver, 303-355-3775
Chef Michael Degenhart just got tired one day after 12 years of *pâté de la maison* at restaurant Tante Louise, so he's opened his own smashingly clean-lined eatery not far away in East Denver, and offers foods that span the northern hemisphere, such as vegetable carpaccio, quail tagine and braised lamb shank – even some French.

Ruth's Chris Steakhouse ◗§   24 | 22 | 23 | $43
1445 Market St. (15th St.), Denver, 303-446-2233
✉ Another contender in the "Denver steakhouse race", this LoDo outpost of the New Orleans–based meatery earns nods for its "very expensive but superb" steaks, "perfect creamed spinach" and "gracious", "personal service"; but crankier carnivores who favor other cow palaces growl it "doesn't measure up": "noisy", "snooty" and "pricey, hoo boy!"; ratings suggest most "can't wait to go back."

Sabor Latino   22 | 17 | 20 | $17
4340 W. 35th St. (Tennyson St.), Denver, 303-455-8664
■ For "the best paella west of Madrid", *vaya* on over to this veteran North Denver Mexican–South American, which relocated a couple of years back; many longtime fans "love" the "new, larger location", as well as its "big portions" of "deliciously unusual" cooking.

Saffron   23 | 18 | 20 | $25
6600 S. Quebec St. (bet. Arapahoe Rd. & Peakview Rd.), Englewood, 303-290-9705
■ "From the look of the place you won't expect much, but you're in for a treat" promise boosters of this Continental–Middle Eastern "surprise" in a Greenwood Village "strip mall"; step inside, and you'll find a "quiet, pretty" setting for "consistent" and "reasonably priced" food served by a "friendly staff" – "they do a nice job at everything."

Sahara Restaurant   22 | 13 | 20 | $19
Arapahoe Station, 9636 E. Arapahoe Rd. (bet. Havana St. & Hwy. 25), Greenwood Village, 303-790-4707
■ "My Moroccan friends rave about" this Middle Eastern confides one of the many fans of this "accommodating" Greenwood Village "gem in a shopping center" in a "Whopper wasteland"; the "appetizers alone would be good" for a meal, but the entrees are "interesting" too.

Señor Pepe's S   22 | 14 | 18 | $14
1422 Poplar St. (E. Colfax Ave.), Denver, 303-321-1911
■ The "best cheap Mexican eats in town" keep 'em coming to this "old standard", a "consistent" East Denver beanery-beefery; sure, the joint's "dated", but it's still a "comfortable" "neighborhood" favorite that stands out "in a city full of Mexican restaurants."

Seoul Food of Korea   20 | 10 | 15 | $13
701 E. Sixth Ave. (Washington St.), Denver, 303-837-1460
■ As the rating suggests, "decor is nil" at this East Denver Korean, but the "tasty" food "is worth a try", if only to answer the question: "how can something this healthy taste this good?"; soul mates love the "good buys", "friendly service" and "outstanding bibimbob."

Ship Tavern S   23 | 25 | 22 | $27
Brown Palace Hotel, 321 17th St. (bet. Broadway & Tremont Pl.), Denver, 303-297-3111
☑ Maties "treasure" "Denver's most atmospheric bar" as a "great hangout" for "classy" but "informal dining" on "good", "honest" American pub fare in an "elegant hotel" that guarantees "impeccable service"; a few who jump ship say she's "living on a past rep" and serving "food without imagination", but that misses the point for those in love with the "nostalgic", "wonderful feel."

Sonoda's S   22 | 15 | 18 | $21
3108 S. Parker Rd. (Dartmouth Ave.), Aurora, 303-337-3800
Centennial Promenade, 9623 E. County Line Rd. (I-25), Englewood, 303-708-8800
■ Enthusiasts say this Aurora and Englewood duo rolls "always terrific" and "fresh" sushi and deserves more kudos for other "wonderful" Japanese dishes; service at the bar is "great", while "service at the tables can be slow", but either way, there's "always a good time" to be had here.

Starfish S   22 | 20 | 21 | $30
300 Fillmore St. (3rd Ave.), Denver, 303-333-1133
☑ Fans of fin and gill still swim to this Cherry Creek seafooder for "creative", "fresh" and "outstanding" fish in a "wonderful ambiance" that includes "great jazz pianists"; foes complain that "the star has fallen far", pointing to a "difficult noise level" and "inconsistent" food and service, but it's hard to go wrong with "cocktails and appetizers."

Stir Crazy Cafe S⊅   21 | 18 | 19 | $15
290 S. Downing St. (Alameda Ave.), Denver, 303-777-8922
■ "Excellent food" "for the price" finds its way to the tables of this Washington Park Pan-Asian earning nods for its "friendly staff", "tasty, big portions" and "appealing modern decor" ("tiny tables" notwithstanding); "even vegetarians and vegans" can find something to like.

STRINGS ⑤
26 | 23 | 24 | $34
1700 Humboldt St. (17th Ave.), Denver, 303-831-7310
☑ "As close to casual but elegant dining as can be had in Denver" claim buffs of this "bright, appealing" and affordable Uptown Cal-Med-American "institution" that's *the* place for "power lunching"; however, there are grumbles about "uneven service."

Sullivan's Steakhouse
23 | 23 | 23 | $39
1745 Wazee St. (18th St.), Denver, 303-295-2664
■ For the "tenderest steaks", "big portions for the price", "terrific service" and "martinis and dark wood", stampede to this LoDo steakhouse, "a newcomer that's hitting on all cylinders"; the few beefs focus on "ridiculous" wine prices and the noise level, but overall, consensus is this is a serious challenge to the "other big name" meateries in town.

Sunny China Cafe ⑤
20 | 10 | 19 | $15
1156 S. Broadway (bet. Arizona & Mississippi Aves.), Denver, 303-722-9968
■ Some say that this South Central spot serves "Denver's only authentic Chinese": it offers two menus, one of more standard, familiar fare, and the other, aimed at its Chinese clientele, that's "more interesting and unusual"; the setting's not fancy, but "portions are hearty" and service is "earnest."

SUSHI DEN ⑤
27 | 24 | 20 | $30
1487 S. Pearl St. (Florida Ave.), Denver, 303-777-0827
☑ This Washington Park high-end Japanese "home to the beautiful people" may be "painfully hip" and as "chichi as they come", but most concur it also "puts the fresh in sushi" and is "worth the wait you'll undoubtedly have"; wet blankets cite "arrogant" patrons and staff and insist "there's better sushi in Denver", but they're loudly overruled by enthusiasts who swear "nothing ever compares."

Sushi Tazu ⑤
24 | 16 | 18 | $25
300 Fillmore St. (E. 3rd Ave.), Denver, 303-320-1672
☑ On "nice days" you can "eat outside" and "people-watch" at this "small" Cherry Creek Japanese, where the "well-executed menu" includes both "excellent cooked food" and "first-rate sushi"; since "service can be very slow", it helps "if you're willing to wait."

Swan at Inverness, The
26 | 25 | 26 | $46
Inverness Hotel & Golf Club, 200 Inverness Dr. W. (County Line Rd., east of I-25), Englewood, 303-799-5800
■ The "elegant", "soothing", "exquisite" setting at this "upscale" Englewood hotel Continental earns clucks and coos aplenty from those who appreciate a "place where you can dress up" and enjoy "outstanding food", "savvy service" and "excellent wines"; though a few quack "company expense accounts only", most trumpet this "very romantic" "place for a celebration."

Swing Thai S   21   17   17 $11
301 S. Pennsylvania St. (Alameda Ave.), Denver, 303-777-1777
■ "Not bad" for "a remodeled gas station" say lovers of this "cute" and "pleasantly hip" South Central Denver fast-food Thai; it's "good for takeout", but "eating there is fun too", with "quick, tasty" dishes served in "good-sized portions" at a "nice price"; some say it's for those who like a "lot of sugar in the sauces and a lot of Sinatra" from the boxes.

Table Mountain Inn S   22   21   20 $23
1310 Washington Ave. (bet. 13th & 14th Sts.), Golden, 303-277-9898
■ After touring Coors Brewery in Golden, you may be in just the right mood for the "excellent and inventive" "high-end" Mexican-SW fare found at this nearby adobe hotel eatery; other pluses include "friendly service", a "great patio for lunch" and "unique decor that matches" the menu.

TANTE LOUISE   27   26   26 $42
4900 E. Colfax Ave. (Eudora St.), Denver, 303-355-4488
■ "A favorite after all these years", this East Denver French veteran still delivers "intimate, romantic dining" and "unpretentious elegance" in a "lovely old home"; "gracious host" Corky Douglass "uncorks a great meal" and "oversees a great wine list", and if a few callow souls consider this "classic" a "fossil", its adoring clientele cherishes it as a "sanctuary for life before baseball caps and jeans."

Taqueria Patzcuaro S≠   23   13   18 $13
2616 W. 32nd Ave. (Bryant St.), Denver, 303-455-4389
■ You can take "a trip to Michoacán" or you can pay a visit to this North Denver "institution" noted for "fresh, tasty" and "terrifically *auténtico*" Mexican chow that's a "great value"; "it doesn't serve alcohol", but check out the homemade "*liquidas frutas.*"

Thai Hiep S   23   14   19 $16
Far East Ctr., 333 S. Federal Blvd. (Alameda Ave.), Denver, 303-922-5774
2690 E. Country Line Rd. (University Blvd.), Littleton, 303-779-9001
■ Notwithstanding the name, these South Denver and Littleton twins serve "great Vietnamese" food at "good prices" in a "very hip" environment; surveyors enjoy the "terrific variety" of dishes on the "nice lengthy menu", and the "amazingly friendly staff" is another reason to return.

Three Sons Restaurant S   21   21   21 $22
2915 W. 44th Ave. (Federal Blvd.), Denver, 303-455-4366
◪ *Molto* bravos greet the "old-style but good, honest" "red-sauce" fare dished up by a "mature staff" at this North Denver Italian; a few cynics may find the pasta "ordinary" and liken the decor to a "Neapolitan fever dream", but most are still charmed by the "extravagant decorations for Christmas" and the "traditional food of yesteryear."

Tivoli Deer Restaurant S

| 25 | 24 | 24 | $38 |

26295 Hilltop Dr. (Hwy. 74), Kittredge, 303-670-0941

☑ Most agree it's worth the "short, scenic drive" to dine at this "charming, rustic" and "unique" Kittredge Continental-Scandinavian offering a "romantic" setting for a "fixed-price", "better-than-average" meal including "all-you-can-drink wine" ("get a room for the night nearby"); although devotees say it's "worth it at any price", a minority calls it "disappointing", with "spotty service."

Tommy's Oriental ⇔

| 23 | 7 | 15 | $12 |

3410 E. Colfax Ave. (Cook St.), Denver, 303-377-4244

■ Heat-seekers soar to this East Denver fast-food Chinese-Thai for "two words: pad Thai" ("the best in town") plus other "real cheap", "fast and great" Asian eats; sure, there's "no decor" – check that rating! – but there are options: dine in, take out or phone for "quick delivery."

Trinity Grille

| 22 | 21 | 22 | $28 |

1801 Broadway (Tremont Pl.), Denver, 303-293-2288

■ Here's "the *Cheers* of Downtown Denver", where the "gentlemen's club" servers "always know your name" and bring to table "old-style" American "chop house" eats (including the "best crab cakes anywhere"); it's "difficult to get a table at lunch", so arrive by 11:30 AM if you don't want to wait.

T-Wa Inn S

| 22 | 13 | 18 | $18 |

555 S. Federal Blvd. (½ block south of Virginia Ave.), Denver, 303-922-4584

■ "Still the best Vietnamese" insist devotees of this South Central Denver spring-roll champion that "sets the standard" with "authentic" dishes sporting "really distinct flavors" (the "pho is worth the trip"); while even fans admit the "decor needs a lift", "reasonable prices" compensate.

T-Wa Terrace S

| 22 | 17 | 18 | $18 |

6882 S. Yosemite St. (2 blocks south of Arapahoe Rd.), Englewood, 303-741-4051

■ Sister to T-Wa Inn, but farther south in Englewood, this "authentic Vietnamese" offers "great ambiance", "tasty" food and "generous portions at lunch"; its location near the Tech Center makes it a "popular business lunch spot", and the "fast service" is good business too.

240 Union S

| 26 | 22 | 24 | $31 |

240 Union Blvd. (3 blocks south of 6th Ave. Frwy.), Lakewood, 303-989-3562

■ It's unanimous: this "underappreciated" New American "jewel" is "hands down the best restaurant on the West Side" of town, serving a "creative", "fabulous" menu (especially "super fish") in a "congenial setting"; it's for "that special night" made better by "superb service" – just beware "the noisy, yuppie lunch crowd."

Vesta Dipping Grill S   22 | 24 | 21 | $29 |
1822 Blake St. (bet. 18th & 19th Sts.), Denver, 303-296-1970
◪ "Smart, sexy and tasty" sum up this LoDo Eclectic,
well regarded for its "inventive, hip and urban" decor and
"awesome", "unique" menu that's "the freshest idea to hit
Denver this decade" (the specialty is skewers of grilled
meat or seafood served with various dipping sauces); those
out of the loop whine that it's "noisy" and "too trendy by
half", but most give a thumbs-up to this "fun place to dip."

Walnut Cafe S   22 | 14 | 19 | $13 |
338 E. Colfax Ave. (Logan St.), Denver, 303-832-5108
■ "Get there early" or be prepared to stand in a long line
at this Downtown diner, where the "coolest", "slightly surly"
but "very colorful" servers sling the "best breakfasts" in
"huge portions" – the "hearty" eats are guaranteed to
work magic on "hangovers."

Watercourse Foods S   22 | 13 | 19 | $12 |
*206 E. 13th Ave. (bet. Grant & Sherman Sts.), Denver,
303-832-7313*
■ New to Capitol Hill in mid-1999, this "New Age–style",
"very affordable" and "friendly" Vegetarian sports a
"thinking" chef who's earning big kudos (and a "place in
Denver's eating scene") for "incredible", "creative" and
"satisfying" eats; it's "people-watching" central, but open
only for breakfast ("the best") and lunch.

Wazee Supper Club ◕S   20 | 19 | 18 | $16 |
1600 15th St. (Wazee St.), Denver, 303-623-9518
■ A "fine, old neighborhood bar" it is, say admirers of this
"smoky, dark" LoDo pizza palace, with "the best pie in the
Mile High City" plus "tough, but good servers" and "a great
jukebox"; "nothing changes here and that's its charm."

WELLSHIRE INN S   23 | 26 | 23 | $34 |
3333 S. Colorado Blvd. (E. Hampden Ave.), Denver, 303-759-3333
◪ Many surveyors like the fact that this South Central
Denver Traditional American doesn't list a "lot of trendy
'new' things" on its menu, just "classics", and serves them
in a "beautiful", "Tudor-style" mansion with "elegant",
"special occasion" decor; the jaded label it "predictable"
and "butler stuffy", but they're outvoted.

Wild Ginger   23 | 17 | 20 | $17 |
399 W. Littleton Blvd. (S. Delaware St.), Littleton, 303-794-1115
◪ "When they say that a dish is hot, take their word for
it" warn regulars of this Littleton Thai, where the spicy,
"authentic" eats can be "hotter than the hubs of hell";
though a few naysayers suggest it's "fallen off of late", most
are still boosters who say that "in spite of the appearance"
("spartan"), the "delicious", "fresh" food and "wonderful"
service add up to an "an incredible value."

Yanni's 🄢   21 | 16 | 20 | $22
*2223 S. Monaco Pkwy. (1 block south of Evans Ave.),
Denver, 303-692-0404*
■ Hellenophiles aver that this Southeast Denver shopping
mall storefront is "the only real place for Greek food" and
note "what a difference an on-site owner makes", pointing
to the "warm" atmosphere and "free shots of ouzo"; with
"lovingly prepared home-style food" and an island feel,
you can "visit Greece in your own neighborhood."

Yia Yia Euro Cafe 🄢   22 | 23 | 21 | $28
*8310 E. Belleview Ave. (DTC Blvd.), Greenwood Village,
303-741-1110*
☑ "Yeah! yeah!" say devotees of this "upbeat", "chichi"
Greenwood Village Mediterranean that's "good for a chain"
with "attractive decor" (including an outdoor patio), "terrific
service" and "yummy", "contemporary" eats; critics retort
no, no, this "quintessential yuppie" spot is too "noisy and
crowded", and passes off "average food in a high-class
setting", but ratings suggest the ayes have it.

Yorkshire Fish & Chips 🄢🚭   23 | 5 | 13 | $10
*7275 Pecos St. (½ block south of Boulder Tpke.), Denver,
303-428-4644*
■ "What a greasy place!" is the "definitive" compliment
for this "most authentic", "veddy British" North Denver
seafood shack and its "scrumptious fish 'n' chips"; expect
"no frills" and "little service", but who cares? – "it's the
closest thing to going to London."

Zaidy's 🄢   20 | 14 | 17 | $15
121 Adams St. (1st Ave.), Denver, 303-333-5336
☑ "Denver's Lower East Side" bark boosters of this Cherry
Creek deli that's "great for breakfast" and "busy, busy,
busy" at lunch; the "classic Jewish recipes" include what
kvellers call "the best latkes anywhere" and "amazing matzo
ball soup", though kvetchers grunt that "prices are too
high" and "the Carnegie, it isn't."

Zenith   – | – | – | M
815 17th St. (bet. Champa & Stout Sts.), Denver, 303-293-2322
When Brasserie Z didn't pan out in the same space – a
dead-on gorgeous former Downtown bank lobby – Denver
top toque Kevin Taylor reincarnated his beloved Zenith; back
on the table are roasted corn soup, sashimi tuna, avocado
terrine and kick-ass mahi mahi, among dozens of Taylor's
New American dishes with a Southwestern splash.

North of Denver

FAWN BROOK INN ⑤   26 | 26 | 26 | $41
P.O. Box 387, Hwy. 7, Allenspark, 303-747-2556
■ Raves all around over this "romantic", "cozy", "divine" "hideaway" in Allenspark where the Continental–Regional American cooking is "memorable" and the "friendly", "attentive" service is practically "perfect"; since it's "always a treat" "it's worth the splurge"; N.B. closed January–mid-February.

Nico's Catacombs   22 | 21 | 24 | $38
115 S. College Ave. (Mountain Ave.), Fort Collins, 970-482-6426
☑ The "thick-mustachioed owner" is Nico Zenfield himself, and he rules this "subterranean" Fort Collins Continental-Italian with a velvet touch; "a favorite for over 25 years", it's known for "elegant dining" backed up by "exquisite service"; a few find the ambiance "outdated" and think "it needs some life", but they're outvoted.

Pulcinella Ristorante ⑤   ▽ 25 | 20 | 22 | $30
First National Bank Plaza, 2100 W. Drake Rd. (Taft Hill Rd.), Fort Collins, 970-221-1444
■ There's no clowning around at this Fort Collins Northern Italian: it's a serious mix of an "upscale", "squeaky-clean" dining room, "fine" staff, "authentic" and "excellent" cuisine and "the best Italian wine list in Colorado"; it may be "a bit self-conscious", but locals "feel lucky" to have it.

Young's Cafe ⑤   23 | 18 | 22 | $22
Crystal Garden Shopping Ctr., 3307 S. College Ave. (bet. Foothills Pkwy. & Horsetooth Rd.), Fort Collins, 970-223-8000
■ Fort Collins and its eateries don't garner much *Survey* attention, but this Vietnamese is a "bright spot", serving "perfectly prepared" dishes, including "quick and tasty lunches", using "fresh ingredients"; the only drawback is that some find the atmosphere a bit "cold."

South of Denver

F | D | S | C

CHARLES COURT S
27 | 27 | 26 | $46

Broadmoor Hotel, 1 Lake Ave., Colorado Springs, 719-634-7711

◪ The Broadmoor's fine dining room in Colorado Springs is a "formal" Continental–New American offering "the perfect getaway for a romantic evening", with a "beautiful view of Broadmoor Lake", an "elegant, comfortable setting" and "consistent, proven" food and service; although casual sorts find it too "costly" and "stuffy", ratings say it all for the majority: a "treat for special occasions."

Craftwood Inn S
25 | 25 | 25 | $37

404 El Paso Blvd. (Manitou Ave.), Manitou Springs, 719-685-9000

■ Diners rave over the "super setting" with a view of Pikes Peak, plus the "charming atmosphere" and "unusual menu" at this "elegant" Regional American in an old mansion near Colorado Springs; specializing in "excellent wild game", it offers "true Western flavor" and "great service" – in all, a "worthy" establishment.

Gabriel's S
25 | 25 | 25 | $35

5450 N. Hwy. 67 (Santa Fe Dr.), Sedalia, 303-688-2323

■ A "charming Victorian setting" "in a house with many rooms" makes for "romantic" dining at this Sedalia Northern Italian with "lovely music on the porch", "decadent meat and cream dishes" and a "beautiful garden"; nitpickers whine "why couldn't they put it closer to the civilized world?", but devotees agree it's "worth" the "pretty drive."

LA PETITE MAISON
27 | 25 | 27 | $34

1015 W. Colorado Ave. (bet. 10th & 11th Sts.), Colorado Springs, 719-632-4887

■ Colorado Springs' oldest French restaurant, set in a "darling house", offers "excellent" "classical" and "innovative" cooking presented "with flair", plus a "nice wine list" and "very good individual service"; it's perfect "for a romantic dinner", although perhaps "a little too cutesy" for a few; P.S. insiders advise "try the pâté and try not to fill up on the bread."

Margarita at Pine Creek, The 🅂   23 | 24 | 22 | $25 |
7350 Pine Creek Rd. (I-25 & Woodmen Rd.),
Colorado Springs, 719-598-8667
■ Named for the flower, not the drink, this Colorado Springs Eclectic-Southwestern dishes up "good", "flavorful" eats in an "Old Mexico" "adobe hacienda" ambiance; it's "quaint and cozy", and a "great place for privacy" ("the tables are widely separated"), with a staff that's "always friendly."

Mataam Fez 🅂   22 | 24 | 23 | $29 |
101 N. Tejon St. (Kiowa Rd.), Colorado Springs,
719-634-2102
See review under Denver & Environs.

Old Stone Church   23 | 23 | 20 | $23 |
210 Third St. (Wilcox St.), Castle Rock, 303-688-9000
■ "Heavenly" say devotees of this Castle Rock Continental that "really is [in] an old church", hence the "unique" decor ("love the stained glass windows"); the "creative food" with "some nouveau touches" plus "cheerful service" make it "great for lunch" when shopping at the nearby and popular outlet mall.

PENROSE ROOM, THE 🅂   25 | 27 | 26 | $45 |
Broadmoor Hotel, 1 Lake Ave., Colorado Springs,
719-634-7711
◪ For a "perfect getaway for a romantic evening", this "beautifully remodeled", pricey Continental–New French atop the Broadmoor offers "tremendous views" of "Colorado Springs and the Rockies" along with "dining the way it used to be": "dressing up elegantly" and "dancing" to a live orchestra while dining on "great food"; but despite high ratings, some gripe about "stuffy", "hovering" waiters.

Boulder & Environs

TOP 3 FOOD RANKING

Restaurant	Cuisine Type
26 John's	Med./New Amer.
Flagstaff House	Continental/New Amer.
Full Moon Grill	Northern Italian

F	D	S	C

Black Bear Inn ⑤   24 | 24 | 22 | $32
42 E. Main St. (2nd Ave.), Lyons, 303-823-6812

■ You'll "think you're in Bavaria" at this "very authentic" Estes Park Continental-German-Swiss, where the decor's "old-world charm" bolsters the "always excellent" cooking; most agree it adds up to a "pleasant meal" that's "worth the drive", despite a few reports that the atmosphere "can be a bit unfriendly."

Boulder Cork ⑤   21 | 19 | 21 | $28
3295 30th St. (bet. Iris Ave. & Valmont Rd.), Boulder, 303-443-9505

■ For "great steak" in the vegetarian capital of the state, those in the know turn to this "time-honored" "old standby", a Boulder seafooder-steakhouse that earns high ratings for its "innovative" menu, including "excellent fish" and "a notable wine list"; it's a "pleasant experience", despite "occasionally spotty service."

Chautauqua Dining Hall ⑤   21 | 22 | 19 | $24
900 Baseline Rd. (9th St.), Boulder, 303-440-3776

■ There aren't too many places where you can dine in "historic" "early Colorado" surroundings, snag a table on a "premier" porch with "breathtaking" views overlooking Boulder, eat "fine", "imaginative" New American food from executive chef Bradford Heap and then "take a walk around a park" after lunch or dinner; then again, there aren't too many restaurants dating from 1898, all of which makes this "unique experience" a "must"; N.B. wine and beer only.

Chipotle Mexican Grill ⑤   20 | 15 | 16 | $9
919 Pearl St. (9th St.), Boulder, 303-544-9383
1100 Ken Pratt Blvd. (Pratt Pkwy.), Longmont, 303-651-6763
See review under Denver & Environs.

Daddy Bruce's Bar-B-Que ⇗   21 | 9 | 16 | $12
2000 Arapahoe Ave. (20th St.), Boulder, 303-449-8890

■ Although the "friendly, sociable" Daddy Bruce Randolph passed away, his "solid", "consistent" pit barbecue still draws lip-lickers to this Boulder 'cue shack, a "dump" that's also an "institution" and "great for takeout" — "where else would one go?"

Dandelion ⑤ | 24 | 23 | 22 | $32 |
1011 Walnut St. (bet. Broadway & 9th St.), Boulder, 303-443-6700
■ "Like its namesake, let's hope it multiplies" wish fans of this Boulder New American that's built a following with truly "innovative", "fresh and flavorful" cooking by chef Kevin Taylor; the room is "beautiful" (despite "too close" tables) and – wonder of wonders in the People's Republic – the "very attentive" service sports "minimal attitude."

Dot's Diner ⑤ | 20 | 14 | 17 | $9 |
1333 Broadway (University St.), Boulder, 303-447-9184
2716 28th St. (Valmont Rd.), Boulder, 303-449-1323 ⑨
☑ Although many think it "lost character when it moved out of the gas station" (and became a duo), this "funky", "classic Boulder hippie hangout" still serves what many say are "biscuits to die for" and "great" corned beef hash to the "Birkenstock crowd"; cynics say "quality is not where it was a few years ago" and gripe about "surly" "servers with nose rings", but you can "count on a wait for weekend breakfast."

European Cafe | 25 | 20 | 22 | $31 |
Arapahoe Village Ctr., 2460 Arapahoe Ave. (bet. Folsom & 28th Sts.), Boulder, 303-938-8250
☑ "Still yummy" is the majority view on this "top-shelf" Boulder American-Continental, despite a few who say it's gone "downhill" since the departure of founding chef Radek Cerny; "superb except for its strip mall setting", it offers "fantastic" food and "wonderful desserts" that make it "popular with academics" who coin a phrase: "eurorific."

Falafel King ⑤ | 18 | 10 | 14 | $9 |
1314 Pearl St. (bet. 13th & 14th Sts.), Boulder, 303-449-9321
See review under Denver & Environs.

Flagstaff House ⑤ | 26 | 27 | 25 | $48 |
1138 Flagstaff Rd. (on Flagstaff Mtn.), Boulder, 303-442-4640
■ Boulder's top "special-occasion" restaurant earns applause for its "elegant" and "imaginative" (albeit "pricey") Continental–New American dining, "amazing wine list" and, especially, for its "fantastic view" of the city below (it's the "best place to take out-of-state visitors" or "someone you love"); while most agree it has "few, if any, flaws", there are gripes about service that's "terribly impressed with itself."

Full Moon Grill ⑤ | 26 | 20 | 23 | $30 |
Village Shopping Ctr., 2525 Arapahoe Ave. (bet. Folsom & 28th Sts.), Boulder, 303-938-8800
■ Admirers wax rhapsodic about this Boulder "hidden gem" from executive chef Bradford Heap, touting the "creative", "superb" Northern Italian menu, "well-organized" wine list and "great service", all of which have "improved with age"; although the "cozy", "funky" space is simply "too crowded" to some and the "irresistible" dishes can be "slow" to arrive, "it's still the place to go casual and feel like a king."

Greenbriar Inn, The S   23 | 23 | 23 | $37

8735 N. Foothills Hwy. (Left Hand Canyon Dr.), Boulder, 303-440-7979

■ Though "old-fashioned and stuffy", this International–New American just outside Boulder is a "longtime favorite" that earns the most praise for its "romantic setting" and "pepped up" decor that are "ideal for a special evening"; but despite equally solid food ratings, many suggest that the menu "has not kept up" and find the fare "not equal to the cost" ("all else very nice"); perhaps a recent chef change will perk up the kitchen.

Healthy Habits S   19 | 12 | 13 | $11

Meadows on the Pkwy., 4760 Baseline Rd. (Foothills Pkwy.), Boulder, 303-494-9177
See review under Denver & Environs.

Jax Fish House S   24 | 19 | 20 | $27

928 Pearl St. (bet. 9th & 10th Sts.), Boulder, 303-444-1811
See review under Denver & Environs.

John's   26 | 22 | 24 | $37

2328 Pearl St. (bet. 23rd & 24th Sts.), Boulder, 303-444-5232
☑ Love is in the air at Boulder's longtime "hidden" Med–New American in a "romantic", "intimate", "softly lit" house where "fine", "solid service" complements the "wonderful" cooking with the "best ingredients" by "one-man show" chef John Bizarro; a few complain that it "hasn't kept up" with the times, but ratings confirm it's still a "special place" for many.

Karen's Country Kitchen S   22 | 20 | 20 | $17

700 Main St. (Pine St.), Louisville, 303-666-8020
☑ A morning "standby" say most about this Louisville American eatery/bakery turning out "terrific sweets" and "yummy breakfasts" in a "charming, charming, charming" setting; for many, the "solid" "homestyle" cooking works best early in the day ("breakfasts are good, dinners blow"), and the "fabulous" weekend brunches are especially popular – "expect a wait."

KT's Hick'ry Pit BBQ   20 | 10 | 16 | $11

7464 Arapahoe Rd. (75th St.), Boulder, 303-786-7608
■ Though it's edged out in the ratings by Daddy Bruce's, pit partisans insist Boulder's "best BBQ" is found at this "friendly" stop where the "great" sauces and ribs are "close to Kansas City 'cue"; the "pig pile sandwich is the best" – "bring napkins."

La Chaumiere S   25 | 24 | 23 | $34

12311 N. St. Vrain Dr. (Hwy. 36), Lyons, 303-823-6521
■ "Fine" Continental-French cuisine and wine are found at this "low-key, informal" eatery between Lyons and Estes Park; it garners "the highest accolades for superb cooking" in a "beautiful setting"; dinner only.

Laudisio 🆂 24 | 19 | 21 | $31
Willow Springs Ctr., 2785 Iris Ave. (28th St.), Boulder, 303-442-1300
⬛ For "excellent" and "beautifully presented" "classic Italian food" and "splendid wines" in a "genteel atmosphere", check out this Boulder old-timer that loyalists call the "best" in the area; although a few gripe that it's "stuck in its ways", most agree it's still a good choice "for special occasions."

Mataam Fez 🆂 22 | 24 | 23 | $29
2226 Pearl St. (22nd St.), Boulder, 303-440-4167
See review under Denver & Environs.

Mediterranean, The 🆂 22 | 21 | 19 | $23
1002 Walnut St. (bet. 9th & 10th Sts.), Boulder, 303-444-5335
⬛ Even on warm winter days, the "very pleasant patio" at this "hip", "funky" Boulder Mediterranean draws a "very attractive clientele" for "people-watching" and chowing down on a "reasonably priced" and "diverse tapas menu" served by "hot waitresses" with "lots of attitude"; "noise is the only downside" because "it's always crowded."

Meritage 🆂 – | – | – | E
Omni Interlocken Resort, 500 Interlocken Blvd. (Hwy. 36), Broomfield, 303-438-6600
Most assuredly the highest-end restaurant between Boulder and Denver, this Broomfield newcomer in the Omni Interlocken Resort is headed up by chef Thomas Ryan (ex the Ritz-Carlton, Aspen); locally made products provide his signature stamp to the Regional American menu.

Orchid Pavilion 🆂 21 | 19 | 19 | $18
1050 Walnut St. (11th St.), Boulder, 303-449-4353
⬛ Admirers toss bouquets for Boulder's "best Chinese", claiming it combines "unusually nice" decor with "above-average" fare and "cordial hosts"; foes, however, insist it's a "pretentious" spot serving merely "adequate food."

Pan Asia Noodle 🆂 22 | 22 | 20 | $21
1175 Walnut St. (Broadway), Boulder, 303-447-0101
⬛ "All aboard" – the "fusion flavors" travel the continent from Japan all the way to Indonesia at this "creative", "funky" Boulder Pan-Asian drawing crowds with its "great blend of flavors" and "fine handrolled noodles"; but even fans admit "some food is great, some average."

Q's 🆂 25 | 24 | 25 | $38
Boulderado Hotel, 2115 13th St. (Spruce St.), Boulder, 303-442-4880
⬛ Despite a drop in ratings since relocating, mavens detect ever more "quality" at this "quintessential" and "complete dining delight", a Boulder New American that delivers "unusually fine dining for a hotel", with "well-constructed", "impeccable" dishes delivered by "attentive" servers in a "handsome" setting; naturally, "it's not cheap", but it's "well worth it."

Ras Kassa's S | 25 | 18 | 20 | $19 |
2111 30th St. (bet. Pearl & Walnut Sts.), Boulder,
303-494-2919
■ The new (1999) "more accessible" location only adds
to the popularity of this "wonderful" Ethiopian "Boulder
institution" that's prized for "fun and flavorful finger food";
it's a perfect "place to bring adventurous diners", just "don't
be surprised when the waiter feeds you the first bite."

Rhumba S | – | – | – | M |
950 Pearl St. (bet. 9th & 10th Sts.), Boulder,
303-442-7771
Chef David Query (of the Jax Fish Houses) turns to de
islands, mon, at this Boulder Caribbean; the eats include
all the jerked meats a sun lover could want, and plenty of
calypso and steel drum music too.

Royal Peacock S | 22 | 18 | 19 | $21 |
5290 Arapahoe Ave. (bet. Conestoga & Range Sts.), Boulder,
303-447-1409
■ "Recommended by people who know and love Indian
food", this "real McCoy" enjoys high praise for its "fantastic
Indian cuisine for everyone" and "attentive", "gracious
service" in a "quiet", "formal environment"; a few quibblers
aside, most agree it's a "wonderful treat."

Rudi's Restaurant S | 22 | 17 | 20 | $21 |
South Creek Ctr., 4720 Table Mesa Dr. (west of I-36), Boulder,
303-494-5858
☑ Boulder folk like this International for its "laid-back"
atmosphere and "gracious service", and even more for its
"always innovative", "unique" vegetarian entrees and "tasty
natural fare" (including hormone-free beef and chicken);
sometimes "the wait is too long", but "the food is great" –
don't miss the "ginger pancakes for breakfast."

Sawaddee S | 22 | 18 | 19 | $18 |
Sunrise Ctr., 1630-B 30th St. (Arapahoe Ave.), Boulder,
303-447-3321
■ The name is a greeting in Thailand, and opens the door
at this well-regarded Boulder Siamese to "delicious", "fresh
and authentic" cooking, with a kitchen that "prepares food
to the level of spice and heat that you request"; patrons
also like the "folksy, earthy atmosphere" of the new
location (early 1999).

Sunflower Natural Fine Dining S | – | – | – | M |
1701 Pearl St. (17th St.), Boulder, 303-440-0220
Everything from the coffee to the wine to the free-range
chicken is organic at this Boulder Eclectic-Vegetarian, which
may satisfy even the strictest vegans, but also cooks tasty
fish and fowl; no red meat or red meat stocks, though.

Sushi Tora S　　　25 | 19 | 20 | $23
2014 10th St. (Pearl St.), Boulder, 303-444-2280
■ "Hands down the best sushi in Boulder" crow fans of this "small, crowded and excellent" Japanese spot known for "quality fish", "large-portioned sushi" and "culinary craftsmanship"; "limited seating" means you should "expect to wait", but despite crowds, the atmosphere remains "friendly" and "low-key."

Sushi Zanmai S　　　22 | 18 | 18 | $27
1221 Spruce St. (Broadway), Boulder, 303-440-0733
◪ For "Boulder's best raw deal", mosey on over to this "lively, fun" Japanese, known as much for its "loud and bustling" atmosphere ("wild parties", "great musical entertainment") as for its top-notch sushi; the raucous air gets to some, though, who gripe that it's "showy," "gimmicky" and "chaotic."

Tom's Tavern S　　　19 | 13 | 18 | $12
1047 Pearl St. (11th St.), Boulder, 303-443-3893
■ When you want "just a good burger" (the "best in the metro area") and "super french fries", this "no-frills" Boulder diner and whimpie joint fills the bill; it "will take you back" to a time when "fast service", "good value" and "nothing fancy" but "good" were the norm.

Trilogy ●S　　　– | – | – | I
2017 13th St. (bet. Pearl & Spruce Sts.), Boulder, 303-473-9463
Identical triplet sisters Jennifer, Jessica and Jill Emich own this late-night (until 2 AM) Boulder wine bar and 'small plate' Eclectic bistro marked by the town's native funkiness, plus live jazz every night except Monday, when they close up shop at midnight.

Trios Winebar & Grille ●S　　　22 | 24 | 22 | $29
1155 Canyon Blvd. (Broadway), Boulder, 303-442-8400
◪ The trio refers to a combo New American restaurant, "impressive" wine bar and (get this) furniture gallery, and the name also plays off the "outstanding" live jazz trios that entertain at this "classy", "festive" Boulder spot; all agree on the "great" wine cellar and ambiance, although comments on the menu range from "superb" to "standard" and the staff strikes some as "pretentious."

Zolo Grill S　　　22 | 19 | 19 | $23
Village Shopping Ctr., 2525 Arapahoe Ave. (bet. Folsom & 28th Sts.), Boulder, 303-449-0444
◪ Hombre, this Boulder Cal-Mex has just about everything: "crowd-pleasing", "super food", a "fun", "relaxed" atmo that appeals to both "young professionals" and "kids", "killer margaritas" and a "separate tequila menu"; critics note that "Boulder's Santa Fe" is also "cacophonous", "inconsistent" and "confuses heat with spice", but most don't seem to mind since it's "always busy."

Ski Areas

ASPEN

TOP 3 FOOD RANKING

	Restaurant	Cuisine Type
27	Renaissance	Med./New Amer.
26	Piñons	Regional American
	Little Nell	New American

	F	D	S	C

Ajax Tavern 🅂
23 | 22 | 19 | $39

685 E. Durant Ave. (Aspen Mtn.), Aspen, 970-920-9333

■ "Sit outside on a beautiful day" urge devotees of the "great patio" at this "casual", "trendy" Aspen Cal-Med that's just inches from Glitter Gulch's biggest mountain; besides "spectacular" views, it offers "top-notch food", "superior presentation" and even "value in a town where it's not necessary", so most put up with "arrogant" servers.

Cache Cache Bistro 🅂
24 | 22 | 22 | $37

205 S. Mill St. (Hopkins Ave.), Aspen, 970-925-3835

■ This longtime Aspen Provençal delivers "the best food for the best price" in Colorado's most expensive town; it's "not overly complicated" either, and the room and service are "unpretentious" to match; "noise" is the only gripe.

Century Room 🅂
24 | 25 | 25 | $45

Hotel Jerome, 330 E. Main St. (Mill St.), Aspen, 970-920-1000

■ Aspen's fine dining secret, this New American in the ur-historic Hotel Jerome "hits all the yum buttons"; "no expense is spared", from the "turn-of- the-century elegance" to the "great food" and "excellent wines" – it all comes at a price, of course, but "they don't rush you."

Conundrum 🅂
– | – | – | E

325 E. Main St. (bet. Mill & Monarch Sts.), Aspen, 970-925-9969

Award-winning toque George Mahaffey (for years at The Little Nell Restaurant) follows the seasons in this tony Aspen New American newcomer, with dishes such as Maine lobster tortelloni luring in the well-heeled.

Krabloonik 🅂
25 | 24 | 23 | $49

4250 Divide Rd., Snowmass Village, 970-923-3953

■ For "exotic meats in a cabin-like setting", adventurous carnivores head to this Regional American at the Snowmass husky training center outside Aspen; it may be "like eating in a high-end kennel", but this game and American wine specialist still conjures up "red meat" heaven; still, krab-a-lot-niks "always feel taken" by the high prices.

Little Nell Restaurant S | 26 | 26 | 26 | $49 |
Little Nell Hotel, 675 E. Durant St. (Spring St.), Aspen,
970-920-6330
■ It's "worth every dollar you will spend" purr enthusiasts of this "very cosmopolitan", "pricey" Aspen hotel dining room, where, despite chef turnover, pampered sybarites continue to enjoy "fantastic" New American fare and a "great wine list" in a "gorgeous, elegant" setting; don't miss the "courtyard for an alfresco lunch" and remember that "Bobby Stuckey is one of America's best sommeliers."

Little Ollie's S | – | – | – | M |
308 S. Hunter St. (E. Hyman Ave.), Aspen, 970-544-9888
See review under Denver & Environs.

Olives – Aspen S | – | – | – | VE |
The St. Regis Aspen, 315 E. Dean St. (Monarch St.),
Aspen, 970-920-3300
Taking its cues from star chef Todd English's other Olives (Boston, Las Vegas and Washington, D.C.), this pricey Aspen Mediterranean in the St. Regis is big on garlic, greens and gumption, with Colorado notes sparking the menu; as with its sibs, this branch has the trademark exhibition kitchen too.

Piñons S | 26 | 25 | 26 | $54 |
105 S. Mill St. (Main St.), Aspen, 970-920-2021
■ "Go for the venison" say boosters of this "pricey" Aspen Regional American attracting an "older crowd" with "excellent game" and other "delicious" fare enhanced by "wonderful service" and "gorgeous" Western decor; though a few gripe that the "menu hasn't changed in 10 years", the majority applauds the fact that it "oozes consistency."

RENAISSANCE S | 27 | 25 | 26 | $57 |
304 E. Hopkins Ave. (bet. Mill & Monarch Sts.), Aspen,
970-925-2402
☑ "Well-heeled clients" shower encomiums on Aspen's toniest Med–New American, giving high marks to its "unbelievably professional staff" and "generally superb", "imaginative and creative" food in a "very elegant" setting that's good for "celebrity watching"; although a few cite occasional "misses" and find it a bit "pretentious", those who can handle the high tabs rate it one of the "best in the state" and a "favorite anywhere."

Syzygy S | 25 | 24 | 23 | $49 |
520 E. Hyman Ave. (bet. Galena & Hunter Sts.), Aspen,
970-925-3700
■ "Wow" – the "beautiful waterfall" and "artfully prepared cuisine in a setting to match" add up to a "romantic" experience that's "very pricey but actually worth it" at this "swanky" Aspen New American, a former haunt of Spider Sabich, among other notables; an "affordable wine list" and "great" live jazz are other pluses.

Takah Sushi S   25 | 19 | 22 | $39
420 E. Hyman Ave. (bet. Galena & Mill Sts.), Aspen, 970-925-8588
■ It's a legitimate query – "how do they get such fresh fish so high in the mountains?" – but it's the norm for this "damned good" Japanese with "Aspen's best sushi", "great wines by the glass" and "incredible people-watching"; some find the ambiance too "raucous" and the space too "tiny", but most "always have a good time."

BRECKENRIDGE AREA

TOP 3 FOOD RANKING

	Restaurant	Cuisine Type
27	Keystone Ranch	New American
26	Alpenglow Stube	Regional American
	Cafe Alpine	Regional American

ALPENGLOW STUBE S   26 | 28 | 26 | $56
Keystone Resort, 154 Soda Ridge Rd. (top of N. Peak Mtn.), Keystone, 970-496-4386
■ Diners yodel in favor of this Keystone Regional American, the country's highest restaurant at 12,000 feet, serving "terrific food in an unforgettable setting", backed up by "impeccable service"; it's "worth the money" for a "blowout celebration" – the gondola ride up and down "is the crème de la crème."

Blue Spruce Inn S   23 | 21 | 22 | $32
20 W. Main St. (Madison St.), Frisco, 970-668-5900
■ Whether you're seeking an "awesome bar", "nice fireside dining", "classic Colorado cuisine" (including "great game") or a "dark, quiet", "romantic, rustic" hideaway, you'll find it at this "dependable" Frisco Regional American; but to some locals, "it seems better in the summer when it's not packed with skiers."

Butterhorn Bakery & Cafe S   22 | 16 | 17 | $11
408 Main St. (4th Ave.), Frisco, 970-668-3997
■ Skiers (and summer folk) race to this Frisco breakfast-and-lunch bakery for "yummy, filling", "healthy entrees" and an "always changing roster" of "wonderful breads, cakes and pastries"; "nice outdoor seating" is another draw.

Cafe Alpine S   26 | 21 | 22 | $29
106 E. Adams Ave. (Main St.), Breckenridge, 970-453-8218
■ In a "town not known for great restaurants", this "clubby" Breckenridge Regional American with a "cozy mountain atmosphere" offers a "creative menu, outstanding presentation, attentive service and a fab tapas bar"; though "pricey", it's "excellent when you want something different."

Hearthstone Restaurant, The ⑤ 23 | 22 | 22 | $31

130 S. Ridge St. (Washington Ave., off S. Main St.),
Breckenridge, 970-453-1148

■ "Awesome mountain views", "consistently good",
"generous servings" of Regional American fare and a
"warm", "inviting" atmosphere add up to "very pleasant"
dining at this "charming Victorian home" in Breckenridge
with a menu featuring aged meats; N.B. lunch is served in
the summer only.

KEYSTONE RANCH 27 | 27 | 27 | $56
RESTAURANT ⑤

Keystone Ranch Resort (2½ mi. west of Hwy. 6), Keystone,
970-496-4386

■ "Elegant, excellent but expensive" are the three Es at
this "must-go" Summit County New American in the "best
setting imaginable" – a "historic ranch home" with "superb
views" of Keystone Valley; although "pricey", consensus is
it's "worth it" for the "gourmet" "prix fixe" meals ("excellent
game"), "impeccable service" and "world-class setting."

Poirrier's Cajun Cafe ⑤ 25 | 20 | 22 | $25

224 S. Main St. (Adams St.), Breckenridge, 970-453-1877

■ It's "worth the drive for the gumbo alone" or perhaps
even the "pure bliss" of the "superb bread pudding" at
this "consistently good", highly rated Breckenridge Cajun
that's like "New Orleans in the Rockies"; while some think
it's a "little pricey for what you get", "all of it is outstanding."

Ti Amo Ristorante ⑤ 24 | 19 | 24 | $29

740 N. Summit Blvd., Frisco, 970-668-1993

■ "How could a little, out-of-the-way place be so good?"
ask admirers who love this Frisco Italian (with a branch near
Vail) for its "hearty", "authentic" cooking and "good staff" –
not to mention "reasonable" prices that make it "affordable
for locals", an uncommon virtue in this Plastic Bavaria.

VAIL AREA

TOP 3 FOOD RANKING

	Restaurant	Cuisine Type
28	Sweet Basil	New American
27	Splendido	New American
	Wildflower	New American

Alpenrose ⑤ 24 | 22 | 21 | $32

Vail Village Inn Plaza, 100 E. Meadow Dr., Vail, 970-476-3194

■ If you'd like to "hobnob with Arnold Schwarzenegger"
when he's in Vail, drop by this "sentimental favorite", a
"charming", "classy" bakery/cafe serving "authentic
German [and Austrian] food" and the "best pastries."

BEANO'S CABIN ⑤ | 25 | 28 | 24 | $51 |
Beaver Creek Resort, 1 Beaver Creek Pl. (Avon Rd.), Avon, 970-949-9090
☑ For a "marvelous, magical" dining experience – complete with a horse-drawn wagon ride in summer or a "romantic" "sleigh ride under blankets" in winter – check out this Vail-area New American hideaway and its "warm dining room atop a mountain"; some say it's a "one-time tourist event" and warn "there are second-mortgage papers at the door to clear the tab", but even cynics agree "ya gotta do it."

Gore Creek Grille ⑤ | 21 | 20 | 19 | $29 |
223 Gore Creek Dr. (Bridge St.), Vail, 970-476-2828
■ Yes, it's surprising to get "excellent raw oysters" in the Rockies, but this New American delivers "great" bivalves along with other "inventive but not overly so" fare on a "beautiful patio" overlooking a roaring creek; prices "aren't bad for Vail" and the place is "casual" and "friendly."

GROUSE MOUNTAIN GRILL ⑤ | 27 | 26 | 25 | $47 |
Beaver Creek Resort, 141 Scott Hill Rd. (Village Rd.), Avon, 970-949-0600
■ "Gorgeous and delicious" sums up this "intimate, quiet" Beaver Creek Regional American with a "great view" of the Valley below, and "extraordinary food, decor and service", plus a "top-notch wine selection", inside; though the "delicious, large portions could serve two people", save room for the "excellent desserts."

Left Bank ⑤ ⃝ | 26 | 23 | 23 | $42 |
Sitzmark Lodge, 183 Gore Creek Dr. (Main St.), Vail, 970-476-3696
☑ It's "the only real French restaurant in the state" maintain advocates of this pricey Vail gastrodome, a "romantic adult" place to enjoy "glorious" cooking and "great service" in a "beautiful setting"; outvoted critics moan that it's "staid" and "they don't know the meaning of service"; N.B. cash only.

Mirabelle | 25 | 25 | 23 | $49 |
Beaver Creek Resort, 55 Village Rd. (Hwy. 6), Avon, 970-949-7728
■ A "lovely", "charming" "old mountain cottage" is home to this "special treat", a Beaver Creek New French "gem" drawing raves for its "exciting, innovative cuisine", "strong wine list" and "impeccable service"; "outstanding in every way", it's "very European" through and through.

Montauk Seafood Grill ⑤ | 25 | 20 | 22 | $36 |
549 Lionshead Circle (Hwy. 6), Vail, 970-476-2601
■ Long Island in Lionshead, just east of Vail, is the feel at this seafood house dishing up "excellent", "top-shelf" fin and gill; most agree both food and service are "always good" (the waiters are "friendly" and "fun") and summer brings outdoor dining on the patio.

Picasso
26 26 25 $51

The Lodge at Cordillera, 2205 Cordillera Way, Edwards, 970-926-2200

■ "It's all perfect, even after Paris" sigh fans who paint a "charming" picture of this "quiet and intimate", high-end Vail Valley French in a "gorgeous setting", with "splendid food and wines to match" and a "romantic" ambiance with fireplace; "it's worth the drive to get there" say those with "magical" memories, and if a few claim "it's inconsistent", they're soundly outvoted.

SPLENDIDO S
27 27 26 $58

The Chateau at Beaver Creek Resort, 17 Chateau Ln. (Scott Hill Rd.), Avon, 970-845-8808

■ This "elegant" New American in an "awesome" setting high above Beaver Creek Valley offers "sublime and creative" food and a "great wine list", delivered by a refreshingly "down-to-earth" staff that will nonetheless treat you "royally"; so while "expensive", the "fully satisfied" majority finds it "worth it" – "save for a very special occasion."

SWEET BASIL S
28 23 24 $40

193 E. Gore Creek Dr. (Bridge St.), Vail, 970-476-0125

■ Whether it's the "ultra hip" cuisine, "well-done service", "great outdoor seating" or the "sound of the river below", the bottom line on this Vail New American is that it "reaches great heights without being unreasonably expensive"; not surprisingly, it's "always crowded" so "make reservations."

Terra Bistro S
24 23 23 $43

Vail Athletic Club, 352 E. Meadow Dr. (S. Frontage Rd., off Hwy. 6), Vail, 970-476-6836

■ The "plain" but "pretty" "modern" decor is a good foil for the "very eclectic menu" at this "consistently good", "very creative" Contemporary American in the Vail Athletic Club; "always a good choice" and "great for entertaining", it may be "the most interesting find in the Vail Valley."

Ti Amo Ristorante S
24 19 24 $29

40928 US Hwy. 6 (Hwy. 24), Avon, 970-845-8153
See review under Breckenridge Area.

WILDFLOWER S
27 27 25 $46

The Lodge at Vail, 174 E. Gore Creek Dr. (base of Vail Mountain), Vail, 970-476-5011

■ Superlatives abound for this "beautiful", "fabulous" and "expensive" Vail New American, with diners throwing bouquets for the "world-class", "superelegant" food, "wonderful service" and "gorgeous" decor with "flowers everywhere"; those in the know say it's "lovely to eat outside [on the patio] in the summer"; in sum, it "sets a standard."

Zino Ristorante ⑤   24 | 23 | 21 | $35
River Walk Ctr., 27 Main St. (Hwy. 6), Edwards,
970-926-0444

■ On your way home from skiing, turn off Interstate-70 at Edwards for "an early evening break" at this "very pleasant" Italian; the braised lamb shanks are "excellent", though some go just for the "nice bar and appetizers", especially the "best roasted mussels."

OTHER MOUNTAIN AREAS

TOP 3 FOOD RANKING

Restaurant	Cuisine Type
26 La Montaña	Mexican/Southwestern
Soupçon	French Bistro
25 Gasthaus Eichler	Continental/German

Campagna ⑤   ▽ 26 | 22 | 23 | $41
435 W. Pacific Ave. (bet. Aspen & Townsend Sts.),
Telluride, 970-728-6190

■ You'll need to "make reservations a month ahead" to snag tables at this "pretty, little" Northern Italian in a "lovely old house" in Telluride; but it's worth the trouble (and "worth the expense") to savor the "warm atmosphere" and "fabulous, innovative" cooking from the husband and wife owners, both obviously "dedicated to their food" and their "great Italian wines."

Cosmopolitan Restaurant ⑤   ▽ 25 | 25 | 25 | $36
Columbia Hotel, 300 W. San Juan Ave. (S. Oak St.),
Telluride, 970-728-1292

Tasting Cellar ⑤   – | – | – | E
Columbia Hotel, 300 W. San Juan Ave. (S. Oak St.),
Telluride, 970-728-1292

■ Hard by Telluride's gondola in the cushy boutique Columbia Hotel, this New American is praised for its "excellent service" and "creative and well-presented" cuisine from chef-owner Chad Scothorn; sommelier Keith Rainville is credited for "outstanding wine pairings" both here and at the adjacent, old world–style Tasting Cellar, where diners can also enjoy Scothorn's cooking in the form of six-course French tasting menus while sampling from a selection of over 350 different wines.

Florindo's   24 | 19 | 21 | $26
721 Grand Ave. (8th St.), Glenwood Springs, 970-945-1245

■ Glenwood Springs' best Northern Italian delivers an *abbondanza* of "authentic" and "outstanding food" that addicts swear is "worth any length of wait" (and, since it's "always busy", there will be one); the trattoria "is small" and "sometimes too loud", but most find it a "wonderful experience" and a "great value at lunchtime."

Fontenot's Cajun Cafe ⑤ ▽ 23 | 16 | 20 | $19
78711 US Hwy. 40, Winter Park, 970-726-4021

◪ Spicy is cool for those who find "authentic, excellent Cajun food" and "old-world service" at this Winter Park jambalaya joint offering "a nice change of flavor for a ski area"; but others are hot under the collar over "small portions" and "amateur help and decor", noting "we should have known better."

Gasthaus Eichler ⑤ 25 | 23 | 22 | $27
Gasthaus Eichler Hotel, 78786 US Hwy. 40, Winter Park, 970-726-5133

■ It "feels like après-skiing in the Alps" at this "lovely", "yummy" Winter Park Continental-German known for "superb cuisine" ("fabulous breakfasts"), "great" ambiance and "alfresco dining by a creek when the weather is right"; service is "excellent" and the only *nein* is that the "wine list is a little pricey."

La Marmotte ⑤ ▽ 26 | 24 | 25 | $39
150 San Juan Ave. (south of Colorado Ave.), Telluride, 970-728-6232

■ "Great chef", "great decor" and "great service" chime diners who "love" the "quality" French cooking at this candlelit mountain refuge in a historic building that once served as Telluride's ice house; decorated with works by local artists, it's an upscale "favorite" just a stone's throw from the gondola; N.B. closed in the spring and fall.

La Montaña ⑤ 26 | 21 | 21 | $29
Village Ctr., 2500 Village Dr. (Après Ski Way), Steamboat Springs, 970-879-5800

■ "Excellent", "upscale" Mexican-SW food is the deal at this "sizeable but cozy, second-story" Steamboat Springs beanery; "unusual combinations" and "pretty presentations" add up to "outstanding" eats so "make reservations."

Peaks, The – Appaloosa ⑤ – | – | – | E
136 Country Club Dr. (Mtn. Village Blvd.), Telluride, 970-728-6800
Peaks, The – Legends ⑤
136 Country Club Dr. (Mtn. Village Blvd.), Telluride, 970-728-6800

Telluride's "luxury" ski resort offers two dining options: Legends, serving American-Continental fare as well as Golden Door Spa cuisine (there's a huge, "fab" branch of the spa on-site) for breakfast and lunch, and Appaloosa, serving dinners showcasing fine Colorado-accented American cooking including plenty of beef; both offer patio dining with spectacular views when the weather allows; N.B. a complimentary gondola ride takes diners into Telluride.

Restaurant on the Ridge 🅂 ＿|＿|＿| M |

Meadow Ridge, 1 E. Meadow Mile (Hwy. 40), Fraser, 970-726-7660

Marvin Bronstein won Denver hearts with his mid-'90s Marvin Gardens, and he's doing it again at this upscale Regional American, serving 'mountain cuisine' with Mediterranean touches; the food is straightforward and clean, but Bronstein layers on flavor, even so.

Soupçon 🅂 26 | 24 | 25 | $36 |

127-A Elk Ave. (bet. 1st & 2nd St. alley), Crested Butte, 970-349-5448

■ "Good things come in small packages" remind *amis* of this "delightful" Crested Butte French bistro; the "heavenly food" transports diners even if "the outside looks like an old garage with pink drapes" – "don't miss" this "real winner."

221 South Oak 🅂 ▽ 25 | 23 | 24 | $39 |

221 S. Oak St. (Colorado Ave.), Telluride, 970-728-9507

■ You can always find your way to this New American and its "imaginatively prepared", "exotically creative" "big-city food" in the "small town" of Telluride 'cause the name is the address of this "cozy" "old house" with a "friendly", "intimate" ambiance that's "like dinner in your aunt's home"; a few sticklers note, however, that the "great flavors" sometimes devolve to the "ultimate in fussy food."

Indexes to Colorado Restaurants

Special Features and Appeals

CUISINES*

American (New)
Ambrosia
Beano's Cabin/V
Beehive
Bistro Adde Brewster
Cafe Bohemia
Century Room/A
Charles Court/S
Chautauqua Dining Hall/B
Conundrum/A
Coos Bay
Cosmopolitan/O
Dandelion/B
Dazzle
European Cafe/B
Flagstaff House/B
Gallery Cafe
Gore Creek Grille/V
Greenbriar Inn/B
Highlands Garden
Hugh's
John's/B
Jou Jou
Kevin Taylor
Keystone Ranch/Br
Little Nell/A
Painted Bench
Peaks/O
Potager
Q's/B
Radex
Renaissance/A
Rialto Cafe
Splendido/V
Strings
Sweet Basil/V
Syzygy/A
Terra Bistro/V
Trios/B
240 Union
221 South Oak/O
Wildflower/V
Zenith

American (Regional)
Alpenglow Stube/Br
Blue Spruce Inn/Br

Buckhorn Exchange
Cafe Alpine/Br
Craftwood Inn/S
Denver Buffalo
Denver Chop Hse.
Emil-Lene's Sirloin
Fawn Brook Inn/N
Fort
Fourth Story
Grouse Mtn. Grill/V
Hearthstone/Br
Krabloonik/A
Meritage/B
Peaks/O
Piñons/A
Restaurant on the Ridge/O
Table Mtn. Inn

American (Traditional)
Annie's Cafe
Assignments
Augusta
Avenue Grill
Bang!
Beano's Cabin/V
Bonnie Brae
Bourbon St.
Breakfast Inn
Briarwood Inn
Brothers BBQ
Davies Chuck Wagon
Dot's Diner/B
Dozens
Duffy's Shamrock
Dumitri's
Egg-Ception
Eggshell & Incredibles
Ellyngton's
Healthy Habits
Healthy Habits/B
Hot Cakes
Johnny's Diner
Karen's Country Kitchen/B
Original Pancake Hse.
Palace Arms
Pete's Kitchen
Ship Tavern

---

* All restaurants are in Denver & Environs unless otherwise noted
(A=Aspen; B=Boulder & Environs; Br=Breckenridge Area;
N=North of Denver; O=Other Mountain Areas; S=South of Denver;
V=Vail Area).

Dim Sum
Empress Dim Sum

Eclectic/International
Cafe Alpine/Br
Cafe Paradiso
Cheesecake Factory
Greenbriar Inn/B
Margarita at Pine Creek/S
Mercury Cafe
Rose's Cafe
Rudi's/B
Rue Cler
Trilogy/B
Vesta Dipping Grill

English
House of Windsor
Yorkshire Fish & Chips

Ethiopian
Ethiopian
Queen of Sheeba
Ras Kassa's/B

French
Bistro Adde Brewster
Cosmopolitan/O
La Chaumiere/B
La Petite Maison/S
L'Auberge Zen
Left Bank/V
Normandy
Picasso/V
Tante Louise
Tasting Cellar/O

French Bistro
Aubergine Cafe
Cache Cache/A
Cafe Bohemia
Chez Michelle
Jou Jou
Le Central
Le Delice
Soupçon/O

French (New)
La Marmotte/O
Mirabelle/V
Papillon Cafe
Penrose Room/S
Rue Cler

German
Alpenrose/V
Black Bear Inn/B
Cafe Berlin
Chinook Tavern
Gasthaus Eichler/O
Golden Europe

Greek
Cafe del Sol
Central 1
Dumitri's
Yanni's

Hamburgers
Annie's Cafe
Avenue Grill
Bistro Adde Brewster
Cherry Cricket
My Brother's Bar
Tom's Tavern/B

Health Food
Healthy Habits
Healthy Habits/B
Sunflower/B

Hungarian
Budapest Bistro

Indian
Gandhi
India's
Royal Peacock/B

Irish
Duffy's Shamrock

Italian
(N=Northern; S=Southern;
N&S=Includes both)
Barolo Grill (N)
Bruno's (N&S)
Buca di Beppo (N&S)
Cafe Jordano (N&S)
Campagna/O (N)
Canino's Trattoria (N&S)
Carmine's on Penn (S)
Cherry Tomato (N&S)
Cucina Leone (N&S)
Florindo's/O (N)
Full Moon Grill/B (N)
Gabriel's/S (N)
Il Fornaio (N&S)
janleone (N&S)

Laudisio/B (N&S)
Nico's Catacombs/N (N&S)
Pagliacci's (N&S)
Pantaleone's (S)
Parisi (N&S)
Pasquini's (N&S)
Pasta Pasta Pasta (N&S)
Pulcinella/N (N)
Ti Amo/Br (N&S)
Ti Amo/V (N&S)
Zino/V (N&S)

Japanese
Banzai
Domo
Japon
L'Auberge Zen
Mori Sushibar
Sonoda's
Sushi Den
Sushi Tazu
Sushi Tora/B
Sushi Zanmai/B
Takah Sushi/A

Jewish
Zaidy's

Korean
Seoul Food

Mediterranean
Ajax Tavern/A
Aubergine Cafe
Beehive
Cafe Paprika
Cafe Paradiso
Cedars
Cucina Leone
Damascus
John's/B
Mediterranean/B
Mel's B&G
Olives—Aspen/A
Palomino
Renaissance/A
Rialto Cafe
Strings
Yia Yia Euro Cafe

Mexican/Tex-Mex
Breakfast Inn
Brewery Bar II
Cafe del Sol
Cherry Cricket

Chez Jose
Chipotle
Chipotle/B
Dora's
El Azteca
El Taco de Mexico
El Tejado
Jalapeño
La Cueva
La Montaña/O
Las Brisas
Rosa Linda
Sabor Latino
Señor Pepe's
Table Mtn. Inn
Taqueria Patzcuaro
Zolo Grill/B

Middle Eastern
Cafe Paprika
Cedars
Damascus
Falafel King
Falafel King/B
Jerusalem
Mataam Fez
Mataam Fez/B
Mataam Fez/S
Saffron
Sahara

Moroccan
Mataam Fez
Mataam Fez/B
Mataam Fez/S

Noodle Shops
J's Noodles
New Orient
Pan Asia Noodle/B
Richard Lee's

Pan-Asian
Little Ollie's
Little Ollie's/A
Pan Asia Noodle/B
Stir Crazy Cafe

Pizza
Basil Doc's
Bonnie Brae
Bourbon St.
Edgewater Inn
Pantaleone's
Parisi

Pasquini's
Pulcinella/N
Wazee Supper Club

Scandinavian
Tivoli Deer

Seafood
Avenue Grill
Boulder Cork/B
Chart House
Cherry Crest Mkt.
Fresh Fish Co.
Jalapeño
Jax Fish House
Jax Fish House/B
McCormick's Fish Hse.
Montauk Seafood/V
New Orient
Starfish
240 Union
Yorkshire Fish & Chips

South American
Cafe Brazil
Las Brisas
Sabor Latino

Southwestern
La Montaña/O
Las Brisas
Margarita at Pine Creek/S
Table Mtn. Inn
Zenith

Spanish
Las Brisas

Steakhouses
Boulder Cork/B
Brook's
Buckhorn Exchange
Chart House
Del Frisco's
Denver Buffalo
Denver Chop Hse.

Emil-Lene's Sirloin
Luke's
Morton's of Chicago
Palm
Peaks/O
Ruth's Chris
Sullivan's Steakhse.

Swiss
Andre's Confiserie
Black Bear Inn/B
Chez Walter

Thai
Busara
J's Noodles
Sawaddee/B
Swing Thai
Tommy's Oriental
Wild Ginger

Vegetarian
(Most Chinese, Indian and
Thai restaurants)
Brewery Bar II
Healthy Habits
Healthy Habits/B
Mercury Cafe
Rudi's/B
Sunflower/B
Watercourse Foods

Vietnamese
Chez Thuy Hoa
Kim Ba
Little Saigon
Long Binh
New Orient
New Saigon
Rose's Cafe
Thai Hiep
Thuy Hoa
T-Wa Inn
T-Wa Terrace
Young's Café/N

LOCATIONS

DENVER & ENVIRONS

ASPEN

Ajax Tavern
Cache Cache
Century Room
Conundrum
Krabloonik
Little Nell

Little Ollie's
Olives – Aspen
Piñons
Renaissance
Syzygy
Takah Sushi

BRECKENRIDGE AREA

Alpenglow Stube
Blue Spruce Inn
Butterhorn Bakery
Cafe Alpine

Hearthstone
Keystone Ranch
Poirrier's
Ti Amo

VAIL AREA

Alpenrose
Beano's Cabin
Gore Creek Grille
Grouse Mtn. Grill
Left Bank
Mirabelle
Montauk Seafood

Picasso
Splendido
Sweet Basil
Terra Bistro
Ti Amo
Wildflower
Zino

OTHER MOUNTAIN AREAS

Crested Butte
Soupçon
Glenwood Springs
Florindo's
Steamboat Springs
La Montaña
Telluride
Campagna
Cosmopolitan

La Marmotte
Peaks
Tasting Cellar
221 South Oak

Winter Park
Fontenot's
Gasthaus Eichler
Restaurant on the Ridge

SPECIAL FEATURES AND APPEALS*

Breakfast/Brunch
(All hotels and the following standouts)
Annie's Cafe
Augusta
Chautauqua Dining Hall/B
Dozens
Dumitri's
Egg-Ception
Eggshell & Incredibles
Ellyngton's
Finster Bros.
Hot Cakes
Il Fornaio
janleone
Original Pancake Hse.
Walnut Cafe
Watercourse Foods
Zaidy's

Business Dining
Bistro Adde Brewster
Brook's
Dazzle
Del Frisco's
Denver Buffalo
Eggshell & Incredibles
Hot Cakes
La Chine
Mori Sushibar
Palace Arms
Palm
Palomino
Papillon Cafe
Radex
Saffron
Ship Tavern
Tante Louise
Trinity Grille
240 Union
Yia Yia Euro Cafe

Caters
(Best of many)
Ajax Tavern/A
Alpenrose/V
Ambrosia

Bistro Adde Brewster
Brook's
Cafe Brazil
California Cafe B&G
Century Room/A
Charles Court/S
Chautauqua Dining Hall/B
Chinook Tavern
Coos Bay
Cucina Leone
Denver Buffalo
Florindo's/O
Gandhi
Grouse Mtn. Grill/V
Hearthstone/Br
Hot Cakes
Il Fornaio
India's
Japon
Jax Fish House
Keystone Ranch/Br
Krabloonik/A
KT's Hick'ry Pit BBQ/B
La Chine
La Montaña/O
Laudisio/B
Le Central
Le Delice
Left Bank/V
Little Nell/A
Luke's
Manor House
Market
McCormick's Fish Hse.
Mediterranean/B
Mirabelle/V
New York Deli News
Original Pancake Hse.
Painted Bench
Palace
Palm
Parisi
Pasta Pasta Pasta
Pulcinella/N
Queen of Sheeba
Rialto Cafe
Saffron

---

* All restaurants are in Denver & Environs unless otherwise noted
  (A=Aspen; B=Boulder & Environs; Br=Breckenridge Area;
  N=North of Denver; O=Other Mountain Areas; S=South of Denver;
  V=Vail Area).

Splendido/V
Strings
Sushi Den
Sushi Tora/B
Sushi Zanmai/B
Table Mtn. Inn
Taqueria Patzcuaro
Tivoli Deer
T-Wa Inn
T-Wa Terrace
Vesta Dipping Grill
Wild Ginger
Zino/V
Zolo Grill/B

Cigar Friendly

Avenue Grill
Bistro Adde Brewster
Black Bear Inn/B
Breakfast Inn
Brewery Bar II
Brook's
Century Room/A
Chinook Tavern
Davies Chuck Wagon
Del Frisco's
Denver Chop Hse.
Dora's
Duffy's Shamrock
Emil-Lene's Sirloin
Greenbriar Inn/B
La Chine
Laudisio/B
Luke's
Manor House
Morton's of Chicago
My Brother's Bar
Normandy
Painted Bench
Palm
Pete's Kitchen
Radex
Rialto Cafe
Rosa Linda
Ruth's Chris
Sullivan's Steakhse.

Trinity Grille
Trios/B
T-Wa Inn
Wazee Supper Club

Dancing/Entertainment

(Check days, times and
performers for entertainment;
D=dancing; best of many)
Beano's Cabin/V (guitar)
Blue Spruce Inn/Br (jazz)
Bourbon St. (jazz)
Buckhorn Ex. (folk/western)
Burnsley/Dining Room (jazz)
Century Room/A (guitar)
Del Frisco's (piano)
Denver Buffalo (varies)
El Azteca (mariachi)
El Tejado (mariachi)
Finster Bros. (bands/readings)
Fourth Story (jazz)
Gabriel's/S (jazz)
Grouse Mtn. Grill/V (jazz/piano)
janleone (piano)
Laudisio/B (piano)
Manor House (piano)
Margarita/Pine Creek/S (varies)
Mataam Fez (belly dancer)
Mel's B&G (bass/piano)
Mercury Cafe (D/bands/DJ)
My Brother's Bar (classical)
Penrose Room/S (D/jazz)
Radex (blues/jazz)
Ship Tavern (cabaret/piano)
Splendido/V (piano)
Starfish (contemporary/jazz)
Sullivan's Steakhse. (jazz)
Sushi Zanmai/B (karaoke)
Swan at Inverness (guitar)
Syzygy/A (jazz)
Table Mtn. Inn (varies)
Trilogy/B (jazz)
Trios/B (jazz)
Vesta Dipping Grill (jazz)
Wellshire Inn (piano)
Zino/V (jazz)

Delivers*/Takeout
(Nearly all Asians, coffee shops, delis, diners and pasta/pizzerias deliver or do takeout; here are some interesting possibilities; D=delivery, T=takeout; *call to check range and charges, if any)
Andre's Confiserie (T)
Annie's Cafe (T)
Avenue Grill (T)
Bang! (T)
Beehive (T)
Bistro Adde Brewster (T)
Breakfast Inn (D)
Brewery Bar II (T)
Busara (D,T)
Cheesecake Factory (T)
Cherry Cricket (T)
Chez Jose (T)
Chipotle (T)
Chipotle/B (T)
Egg-Ception (D,T)
El Taco de Mexico (T)
Gandhi (D,T)
Hot Cakes (D,T)
Karen's Country Kitchen/B (D,T)
Krabloonik/A (D)
Le Delice (D,T)
Market (D,T)
Royal Peacock/B (D,T)
Rudi's/B (D,T)
Stir Crazy Cafe (D,T)
Table Mtn. Inn (D,T)
Watercourse Foods (D,T)
Zaidy's (D,T)

Dessert/Ice Cream
Alpenrose/V
Andre's Confiserie
Bourbon St.
Cucina Leone
House of Windsor
Hugh's
janleone
Jou Jou
La Petite Maison/S
Mirabelle/V
Painted Bench
240 Union

Dining Alone
(Other than hotels, coffee shops, sushi bars and places with counter service)
Campagna/O
Cedars
Le Central
Mirabelle/V
Painted Bench
Poirrier's/Br
Richard Lee's
Trinity Grille
Watercourse Foods

Fireplaces
Alpenglow Stube/Br
Barolo Grill
Beano's Cabin/V
Black Bear Inn/B
Blue Spruce Inn/Br
Boulder Cork/B
Briarwood Inn
Cafe Alpine/Br
California Cafe B&G
Century Room/A
Chez Michelle
Craftwood Inn/S
Dora's
Fort
Greenbriar Inn/B
Grouse Mtn. Grill/V
Il Fornaio
Keystone Ranch/Br
Krabloonik/A
La Chaumiere/B
Las Brisas
Le Central
Manor House
Mirabelle/V
Normandy
Penrose Room/S
Splendido/V
Tante Louise
Wellshire Inn

Health/Spa Menus
(Most places cook to order to meet any dietary request; call in advance to check; almost all Chinese, Indian and other ethnics have health-conscious meals, as do the following)
Augusta
Cafe Paprika

Chautauqua Dining Hall/B
Dot's Diner/B
Dumitri's
Egg-Ception
Healthy Habits
Healthy Habits/B
Renaissance/A
Sonoda's

Historic Interest
(Year opened; *building)
1873 My Brother's Bar*
1879 Greenbriar Inn/B*
1886 Hearthstone/Br*
1889 Century Room/A*
1892 Ellyngton's*
1892 Palace Arms*
1892*/1934 Ship Tavern
1893 Buckhorn Exchange
1898 Chautauqua Dining Hall/B*
1920 janleone*
1934 Bonnie Brae
1946 Pagliacci's
1947 Blue Spruce Inn/Br
1948 Flagstaff House/B

Hotel Dining
Boulderado Hotel
  Q's/B
Broadmoor Hotel
  Charles Court/S
  Penrose Room/S
Brown Palace Hotel
  Ellyngton's
  Palace Arms
  Ship Tavern
Burnsley Hotel
  Burnsley/Dining Room
Columbia Hotel
  Cosmopolitan/O
  Tasting Cellar/O
Gasthaus Eichler Hotel
  Gasthaus Eichler/O
Hotel Jerome
  Century Room/A
Hotel Teatro
  Jou Jou
  Kevin Taylor
Inverness Hotel & Golf Club
  Swan at Inverness
Little Nell Hotel
  Little Nell/A
Oxford Hotel
  McCormick's Fish Hse.

Westin Hotel
  Augusta
  Palm

"In" Places
Aubergine Cafe
Avenue Grill
Bang!
Barolo Grill
Cafe Brazil
Carmine's on Penn
Dandelion/B
Denver Chop Hse.
Fourth Story
Full Moon Grill/B
Gore Creek Grille/V
Hugh's
Japon
Jax Fish House
Kevin Taylor
Keystone Ranch/Br
Little Nell/A
Mel's B&G
Palm
Pan Asia Noodle/B
Papillon Cafe
Potager
Radex
Strings
Sushi Den
Sushi Zanmai/B
Sweet Basil/V
Vesta Dipping Grill
Zolo Grill/B

Jacket Required
Charles Court/S
Morton's of Chicago
Palace Arms
Penrose Room/S

Late Late – After 12:30
(All hours are AM)
Duffy's Shamrock (1:15)
Jerusalem (4)
Mercury Cafe (2)
My Brother's Bar (1:30)
Wazee Supper Club (1)

Noteworthy Newcomers (11)
Ambrosia
Beehive
Busara
Domo

Kevin Taylor
Olives—Aspen/A
Painted Bench
Radex
Rue Cler
Sunflower/B
Trilogy/B

Noteworthy Closings (8)

Bella Ristorante, LoDo
Chives
Cliff Young's
15 Degrees
Moondance
Pacific Star
Sfuzzi
Shrine Mtn. Inn

Offbeat

Assignments
Bourbon St.
Brewery Bar II
Buckhorn Exchange
Cafe Brazil
Cafe Jordano
Denver Buffalo
Domo
El Taco de Mexico
Fort
Gasthaus Eichler/O
India's
Krabloonik/A
KT's Hick'ry Pit BBQ/B
Maria's
Mercury Cafe
Mori Sushibar
My Brother's Bar
Old Stone Church/S
Painted Bench
Pete's Kitchen
Poirrier's/Br
Saffron
Sushi Zanmai/B
Taqueria Patzcuaro
Vesta Dipping Grill
Walnut Cafe
Watercourse Foods
Yorkshire Fish & Chips

Outdoor Dining

(G=garden; P=patio;
S=sidewalk; T=terrace;
W=waterside; best of many)
Ajax Tavern/A (P)
Alpenglow Stube/Br (T)

Alpenrose/V (P)
Ambrosia (P)
Bistro Adde Brewster (P)
Black Bear Inn/B (T)
Bourbon St. (P)
Buckhorn Exchange (P)
Butterhorn Bakery/Br (P)
Cache Cache/A (P)
Cafe Alpine/Br (P)
Cafe Berlin (P)
Cafe Paradiso (P)
Campagna/O (P)
Carmine's on Penn (P,S)
Century Room/A (G,P)
Cosmopolitan/O
Craftwood Inn/S (G,P,T)
Cucina Leone (P)
Denver Buffalo (P)
Denver Chop Hse. (P)
Domo (G,P)
Falafel King (P,T)
Falafel King/B (S)
Full Moon Grill/B (P)
Gasthaus Eichler/O (P)
Gore Creek Grille/V (T,W)
Greenbriar Inn/B (G,P)
Grouse Mtn. Grill/V (T)
Hearthstone/Br (P)
Highlands Garden (G,P)
Jax Fish House (P)
Jax Fish House/B (P)
Keystone Ranch/Br (P)
La Marmotte/O
Laudisio/B (P)
Le Central (T)
Little Nell/A (P)
Margarita at Pine Creek/S (G,P)
Maria's (G)
Market (S)
Mediterranean/B (P)
Mel's B&G (P)
Mirabelle/V (P)
Montauk Seafood/V (P)
Peaks/O
Poirrier's/Br (P)
Potager (G,P)
Pulcinella/N (P)
Renaissance/A (P)
Rialto Cafe (P,S)
Splendido/V (P)
Starfish (P)
Strings (P)
Sushi Tazu (P)

Sushi Zanmai/B (P)
Sweet Basil/V (P)
Table Mtn. Inn (P)
Tante Louise (P)
Terra Bistro/V (P)
Tivoli Deer (P)
240 Union (P)
Vesta Dipping Grill (P)
Wellshire Inn (P)
Yia Yia Euro Cafe (P)
Zaidy's (P)
Zino/V (P,W)

Outstanding Views

Ajax Tavern/A
Alpenglow Stube/Br
Beano's Cabin/V
Charles Court/S
Chart House
Chautauqua Dining Hall/B
Flagstaff House/B
Grouse Mtn. Grill/V
Hearthstone/Br
Keystone Ranch/Br
Krabloonik/A
La Chaumiere/B
Manor House
Penrose Room/S
Splendido/V
Wildflower/V

Parking/Valet

(V=valet parking;
*=validated parking)
Aubergine Cafe*
Avenue Grill (V)
Barolo Grill (V)
Beano's Cabin/V*
Briarwood Inn (V)
Brook's (V)
California Cafe B&G (V)
Carmine's on Penn (V)
Century Room/A (V)*
Charles Court/S (V)
Cheesecake Factory (V)
Del Frisco's (V)
Denver Buffalo (V)
Denver Chop Hse. (V)
Ellyngton's (V)
Flagstaff House/B (V)
Fourth Story*
Fresh Fish Co. (V)
Grouse Mtn. Grill/V (V)
Il Fornaio (V)*

Jou Jou (V)
Kevin Taylor (V)
Keystone Ranch/Br (V)*
Little Nell/A (V)*
Mediterranean/B*
Mel's B&G (V)
Mori Sushibar (V)
Morton's of Chicago (V)
Normandy (V)
Palace Arms (V)
Palm (V)
Papillon Cafe (V)
Penrose Room/S (V)
Radex (V)
Rialto Cafe (V)
Ruth's Chris (V)
Saffron (V)
Ship Tavern (V)
Splendido/V (V)
Strings (V)
Sullivan's Steakhse. (V)
Sushi Den (V)
Swan at Inverness (V)
Tante Louise (V)
Trios/B*
Vesta Dipping Grill (V)
Wildflower/V (V)
Yia Yia Euro Cafe (V)

Parties & Private Rooms

(Any nightclub or restaurant
charges less at off-times;
* indicates private rooms
available; best of many)
Alpenglow Stube/Br
Avenue Grill*
Barolo Grill*
Beehive*
Black Bear Inn/B*
Boulder Cork/B*
Brook's*
Buckhorn Exchange
California Cafe B&G*
Chautauqua Dining Hall/B*
Chinook Tavern*
Coos Bay*
Dazzle
Del Frisco's*
Denver Buffalo
Denver Chop Hse.*
Empress Dim Sum
Flagstaff House/B
Fort
Gabriel's/S

Grouse Mtn. Grill/V
Hearthstone/Br
Hot Cakes
Il Fornaio
Imperial*
India's*
janleone
Johnny's Diner*
Kevin Taylor
Keystone Ranch/Br
Krabloonik/A
KT's Hick'ry Pit BBQ/B*
La Chaumiere/B*
La Chine*
La Petite Maison/S
Laudisio/B
Le Central
Little Nell/A
Manor House*
Mataam Fez*
McCormick's Fish Hse.*
Mediterranean/B*
Mel's B&G
Mercury Cafe*
Mori Sushibar
Morton's of Chicago
New York Deli News
Original Pancake Hse.*
Painted Bench
Palace*
Palm*
Rialto Cafe
Ruth's Chris*
Saffron*
Starfish
Strings
Sullivan's Steakhse.
Syzygy/A
Table Mtn. Inn
Tante Louise*
Trios/B
240 Union
Wellshire Inn
Wild Ginger*

People-Watching

Ajax Tavern/A
Avenue Grill
Bang!
Barolo Grill
Bistro Adde Brewster
Cache Cache/A
Century Room/A
Duffy's Shamrock

Jax Fish House
Left Bank/V
Little Nell/A
Market
Mel's B&G
Montauk Seafood/V
Morton's of Chicago
Palm
Papillon Cafe
Piñons/A
Potager
Q's/B
Renaissance/A
Strings
Sushi Den
Sweet Basil/V
Syzygy/A
Terra Bistro/V
Vesta Dipping Grill
Watercourse Foods

Power Scenes

Ajax Tavern/A
Barolo Grill
Bistro Adde Brewster
Brook's
Del Frisco's
Kevin Taylor
Left Bank/V
Mel's B&G
Palace Arms
Palm
Piñons/A
Renaissance/A
Ruth's Chris
Strings
Sullivan's Steakhse.
Sweet Basil/V
Syzygy/A
Trinity Grille

Pre-Theater Dining

(Call to check prices,
days and times)
Gasthaus Eichler/O
Karen's Country Kitchen/B
La Petite Maison/S
Left Bank/V
Montauk Seafood/V
New York Deli News
Rialto Cafe

Post-Theater Dining
(Call to check prices,
days and times)
Ambrosia
Dazzle
Jou Jou
Left Bank/V
Mirabelle/V
Radex
Rialto Cafe

Prix Fixe Menus
(Call to check prices,
days and times)
Chez Michelle
Chez Walter
Healthy Habits
Keystone Ranch/Br
Laudisio/B
Little Nell/A
Margarita at Pine Creek/S
Mirabelle/V
Pantaleone's
Poirrier's/Br
Renaissance/A

Quiet Conversation
Aubergine Cafe
Briarwood Inn
Campagna/O
Canino's Trattoria
Highlands Garden
janleone
Soupçon/O
Tante Louise

Reservations Essential
Ajax Tavern/A
Beano's Cabin/V
Cache Cache/A
Cafe Alpine/Br
Fort
Grouse Mtn. Grill/V
Krabloonik/A
Left Bank/V
Papillon Cafe
Penrose Room/S
Takah Sushi/A
Tante Louise

Romantic Spots
Aubergine Cafe
Black Bear Inn/B
Briarwood Inn

Bruno's
Budapest Bistro
Cache Cache/A
Cafe Bohemia
Cafe Paradiso
Campagna/O
Canino's Trattoria
Chautauqua Dining Hall/B
Fawn Brook Inn/N
Flagstaff House/B
Fort
Fourth Story
Gabriel's/S
Greenbriar Inn/B
Grouse Mtn. Grill/V
Highlands Garden
Hugh's
janleone
John's/B
Kevin Taylor
La Chaumiere/B
Little Saigon
Manor House
Mirabelle/V
Old Stone Church/S
Palace Arms
Penrose Room/S
Saffron
Sawaddee/B
Soupçon/O
Splendido/V
Syzygy/A
Tante Louise
Tivoli Deer
Trios/B
Wellshire Inn

Saturday – Best Bets
(B=brunch; L=lunch;
best of many)
Briarwood Inn (B,L)
California Cafe B&G (B,L)
Chautauqua Dining Hall/B (B,L)
Cheesecake Factory (B,L)
Ellyngton's (B,L)
Fresh Fish Co. (B,L)
Gallery Cafe (B,L)
Gandhi (B,L)
Hot Cakes (B,L)
Il Fornaio (B,L)
Jou Jou (B,L)
Le Central (B)
Market (B,L)
McCormick's Fish Hse. (B,L)

Mercury Cafe (B)
New York Deli News (B,L)
Pete's Kitchen (B,L)
Strings (B,L)
Tivoli Deer (B,L)
Watercourse Foods (B,L)
Zolo Grill/B (B,L)

Sunday – Best Bets
(B=brunch; L=lunch;
D=dinner; plus all hotels
and most Asians)
Ajax Tavern/A (L,D)
Alpenglow Stube/Br (L,D)
Alpenrose/V (L,D)
Annie's Cafe (L,D)
Avenue Grill (L,D)
Bonnie Brae (L,D)
Boulder Cork/B (L,D)
Breakfast Inn (L,D)
Briarwood Inn (B,L,D)
Busara (L,D)
Cafe Alpine/Br (L,D)
Cafe del Sol (L,D)
California Cafe B&G (B,L,D)
Century Room/A (B,L,D)
Chautauqua Dining/B (B,L,D)
Cheesecake Factory (B,L,D)
Chef's Noodle Hse. (L,D)
Cherry Cricket (L,D)
Cucina Leone (B,L,D)
Damascus (L,D)
Davies Chuck Wagon (L,D)
Denver Chop Hse. (L,D)
Duffy's Shamrock (L,D)
Edgewater Inn (L,D)
El Taco de Mexico (L,D)
El Tejado (L,D)
Empress Dim Sum (L,D)
Ethiopian (L,D)
Fontenot's/O (L,D)
Fourth Story (B)
Fresh Fish Co. (B,L,D)
Gallery Cafe (B,L)
Gandhi (B,L,D)
Gasthaus Eichler/O (L,D)
Golden Europe (L,D)
Gore Creek Grille/V (L,D)
Greenbriar Inn/B (B,D)
Hearthstone/Br (L,D)
Hot Cakes (B,L)
Il Fornaio (B,L,D)
India's (L,D)
janleone (B)

Jerusalem (L,D)
Jou Jou (B,L,D)
J's Noodles (L,D)
Keystone Ranch/Br (L,D)
La Chine (L,D)
Las Brisas (L,D)
L'Auberge Zen (L,D)
Le Central (B,D)
Little Ollie's/A (L,D)
Long Binh (L,D)
Market (B,L,D)
McCormick's Fish Hse. (B,L,D)
Mercury Cafe (B,D)
New Orient (L,D)
New Saigon (L,D)
New York Deli News (B,L,D)
Orchid Pavilion/B (L,D)
Palace (L,D)
Palace Arms (L,D)
Palm (L,D)
Palomino (L,D)
Pan Asia Noodle/B (L,D)
Pasquini's (L,D)
Pete's Kitchen (L,D)
Ras Kassa's/B (L,D)
Rialto Cafe (B,D)
Richard Lee's (L,D)
Rosa Linda (L,D)
Rudi's/B (B,D)
Sawaddee/B (L,D)
Señor Pepe's (L,D)
Ship Tavern (L,D)
Sonoda's (L,D)
Stir Crazy Cafe (L,D)
Sunny China Cafe (L,D)
Sushi Den (L,D)
Sushi Tazu (L,D)
Sushi Tora/B (L,D)
Sushi Zanmai/B (L,D)
Sweet Basil/V (L,D)
Swing Thai (L,D)
Table Mtn. Inn (B,L,D)
Thai Hiep (L,D)
Thuy Hoa (L,D)
Tivoli Deer (B,L,D)
Tom's Tavern/B (L,D)
Trios/B (B,D)
T-Wa Inn (L,D)
T-Wa Terrace (L,D)
Wazee Supper Club (L,D)
Wellshire Inn (B,D)
Yanni's (L,D)
Yia Yia Euro Cafe (L,D)
Yorkshire Fish & Chips (L,D)

Young's Café/N (L,D)
Zolo Grill/B (B,L,D)

Senior Appeal
Alpenrose/V
Andre's Confiserie
Annie's Cafe
Blue Spruce Inn/Br
Charles Court/S
Chez Walter
Chinook Tavern
Fresh Fish Co.
Healthy Habits
Healthy Habits/B
La Petite Maison/S
New York Deli News
Normandy
Pagliacci's
Ship Tavern
Wellshire Inn

Singles Scenes
Avenue Grill
Cherry Cricket
Denver Chop Hse.
Dot's Diner/B
Jax Fish House
Jax Fish House/B
Pan Asia Noodle/B
Potager
Sushi Den
Vesta Dipping Grill
Watercourse Foods
Zolo Grill/B

Sleepers
(Good to excellent food,
but little known)
Campagna/O
El Azteca
Grouse Mtn. Grill/V
House of Windsor
La Chaumiere/B
La Montaña/O
Little Saigon
Luke's
Margarita at Pine Creek/S
Maria's
Painted Bench
Parisi
Pulcinella/N
Queen of Sheeba
Sahara
Señor Pepe's

Soupçon/O
Sunny China Cafe
Taqueria Patzcuaro

Teenagers & Other Youthful Spirits
Mercury Cafe
Pantaleone's
Pete's Kitchen

Visitors on Expense Accounts
Barolo Grill
Beano's Cabin/V
Fort
Kevin Taylor
Keystone Ranch/Br
Krabloonik/A
Left Bank/V
Morton's of Chicago
Palace Arms
Palm
Papillon Cafe
Penrose Room/S
Piñons/A
Renaissance/A
Splendido/V
Swan at Inverness
Sweet Basil/V
Syzygy/A
Tante Louise
Wildflower/V

Wheelchair Access
(Most places now have
wheelchair access; call in
advance to check)

Wine/Beer Only
Annie's Cafe
Beehive
Cafe Berlin
Cafe Brazil
Cafe Jordano
Chautauqua Dining Hall/B
Chipotle
Chipotle/B
Cucina Leone
Domo
Golden Europe
Healthy Habits
Healthy Habits/B
Jalapeño
Kim Ba
New York Deli News

Pantaleone's
Potager
Rosa Linda
Rose's Cafe
Rudi's/B
Sawaddee/B
Seoul Food
Sushi Tora/B

Winning Wine Lists

Barolo Grill
Beano's Cabin/V
Cafe Alpine/Br
Campagna/O
Charles Court/S
Del Frisco's
Flagstaff House/B
Fourth Story
Highlands Garden
Kevin Taylor
Keystone Ranch/Br
Krabloonik/A
Laudisio/B
Le Central
Left Bank/V
Little Nell/A
Mel's B&G
Mirabelle/V
Montauk Seafood/V
Morton's of Chicago
Palace Arms
Papillon Cafe
Penrose Room/S
Piñons/A
Potager
Renaissance/A
Splendido/V
Sullivan's Steakhse.
Swan at Inverness
Sweet Basil/V
Syzygy/A
Tante Louise
240 Union
Wildflower/V

Worth a Trip

Aspen
    Century Room/A
    Little Nell/A
    Renaissance/A
Aurora
    Emil-Lene's Sirloin
Avon
    Grouse Mtn. Grill/V

Boulder
    Flagstaff House/B
Colorado Springs
    La Petite Maison/S
Denver
    Buckhorn Exchange
    Denver Buffalo
    Domo
Keystone
    Alpenglow Stube/Br
    Keystone Ranch/Br
Lyons
    La Chaumiere/B
Morrison
    Fort
Vail
    Sweet Basil/V

Young Children

(Besides the normal fast-food places; * indicates children's menu available)
Ajax Tavern/A*
Alpenglow Stube/Br*
Alpenrose/V*
Annie's Cafe*
Augusta*
Beano's Cabin/V*
Blue Spruce Inn/Br*
Bonnie Brae*
Boulder Cork/B*
Bourbon St.*
Breakfast Inn*
Bruno's*
Cache Cache/A*
Century Room/A*
Chautauqua Dining Hall/B*
Cherry Cricket*
Cherry Tomato*
Denver Buffalo*
Dora's*
Duffy's Shamrock*
Dumitri's*
Egg-Ception*
Eggshell & Incredibles*
El Azteca*
Emil-Lene's Sirloin*
Florindo's/O*
Fontenot's/O*
Fort*
Fourth Story*
Gallery Cafe*
Golden Europe*
Gore Creek Grille/V*

Utah's Most Popular

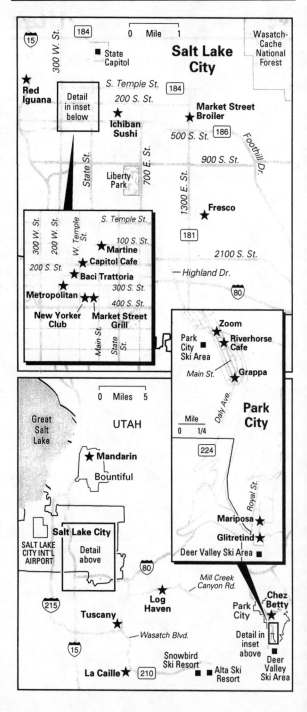

0 Mile 1

Salt Lake City

Wasatch-Cache National Forest

300 W. St.
184
15

★ **Red Iguana**

Detail in inset below

■ State Capitol

S. Temple St. 184
200 S. St.

★ **Market Street Broiler**

500 S. St. 186

Foothill Dr.

★ **Ichiban Sushi**

900 S. St.

State St.

700 E. St.

1300 E. St.

Liberty Park

★ **Fresco**

181

2100 S. St.

S. Temple St.

100 S. St.

— Highland Dr.

300 W. St.
200 W. St.
W. Temple St.

80

★ **Martine**
★ **Capitol Cafe**

200 S. St.

★ **Baci Trattoria**

300 S. St.

Metropolitan ★★
400 S. St.

New Yorker Club   **Market Street Grill**

Main St.
State St.

★ **Zoom**

■ Park City Ski Area

★ **Riverhorse Cafe**

Main St.

★ **Grappa**

Daly Ave.

Park City

Mile
0   1/4

224

0   Miles   5

UTAH

Great Salt Lake

★ **Mandarin**

Bountiful

Salt Lake City

Detail above

SALT LAKE CITY INT'L AIRPORT

80

Royal St.

★ **Mariposa**

★ **Glitretind**

■ Deer Valley Ski Area

215

★ **Tuscany**

★ **Log Haven**

Mill Creek Canyon Rd.

Park City

★ **Chez Betty**

— Wasatch Blvd.

Detail in inset above

15

Snowbird Ski Resort

★ **La Caille**   210

■ ■ Alta Ski Resort

Deer Valley Ski Area

Utah's Most Popular Restaurants*

Each of our reviewers has been asked to name his or her five favorite restaurants. The 20 spots most frequently named, in order of their popularity, are:

1. New Yorker Club
2. Fresco
3. Log Haven
4. Tuscany
5. Metropolitan
6. Mariposa/P
7. Mandarin/G
8. Market Street Broiler
9. Baci Trattoria
10. Market Street Grill
11. Glitretind/P
12. La Caille
13. Chez Betty/P
14. Red Iguana**
15. Grappa/P
16. Capitol Cafe
17. Ichiban Sushi
18. Riverhorse Cafe/P
19. Martine
20. Zoom/P

It's obvious that many of the restaurants on the above list are among the most expensive, but Utah diners also love a bargain. Were popularity calibrated to price, we suspect that a number of other restaurants would join the above ranks. Thus, we have listed 20 Best Buys on page 99.

---

* All restaurants are in Salt Lake City & Environs unless otherwise noted (C=Cottonwood Canyons; G=Greater Utah; P=Park City/Deer Valley/Heber area; S=Sundance).
** Tied with the restaurant listed directly above it.

Top Ratings*

Top 20 Food Ranking

27 Fresco
   Grapevine/G
   Mariposa/P
26 New Yorker Club
   Glitretind/P
   Martine
   Spencer's
   Chez Betty/P
   Ichiban Sushi
   Metropolitan

   Center Cafe/G
25 Red Iguana
   Seafood Buffet/P
   Sundance Tree Room/S
   Yurt, The/C
   Sakura Sushi
   Market Street Grill
   Mandarin/G
   Shallow Shaft/C
   Log Haven

Top Spots by Cuisine

American (New)
27 Mariposa/P
26 Glitretind/P
   Martine
   Metropolitan
25 Log Haven

American (Regional)
25 Sundance Tree Room/S
   Shallow Shaft/C
24 Chimayo/P
23 Zoom/P
   Foundry Grill/S

American (Traditional)
26 New Yorker Club
   Spencer's
   Chez Betty/P
25 Yurt, The/C
24 Goldener Hirsch/P

Brunch
26 Glitretind/P
24 Goldener Hirsch/P
23 Tuscany
   Foundry Grill/S

Continental
27 Grapevine/G
26 New Yorker Club
   Chez Betty/P
24 Goldener Hirsch/P
23 Capitol Cafe

Eclectic/International
26 Center Cafe/G
25 Log Haven
23 Capitol Cafe
21 Oasis Cafe

Hotel Dining
26 Glitretind/P
   Stein Eriksen Lodge
   Spencer's
   Doubletree Hotel
   Chez Betty/P
   Copperbottom Inn
25 Sundance Tree Room/S
   Sundance Resort
24 Goldener Hirsch/P
   Goldener Hirsch Inn

Italian
27 Fresco
24 Caffé Molise
   Primo
   Michelangelo
   Grappa/P

Japanese/Asian
26 Ichiban Sushi
25 Sakura Sushi
24 Cafe Trang
23 Ginza
22 Bangkok Thai

* Excluding restaurants with low voting; all restaurants are in Salt
  Lake City & Environs unless otherwise noted (C=Cottonwood
  Canyons; G=Greater Utah; P=Park City/Deer Valley/Heber area;
  S=Sundance).

               www.zagat.com

Lunch Spots
26 New Yorker Club
    Martine
25 Red Iguana
    Market Street Grill
24 Market Street Oyster Bar

Seafood
25 Seafood Buffet/P
    Market Street Grill
24 Market Street Oyster Bar
    Market Street Broiler
23 350 Main/P

Ski Resort Dining
27 Mariposa/P
26 Glitretind/P
25 Seafood Buffet/P
    Sundance Tree Room/S
    Yurt, The/C

Southwestern
25 Shallow Shaft/C
24 Chimayo/P
21 Red Butte Cafe

Steakhouses
26 Spencer's
22 Maddox Ranch House/G
21 Rodizio Grill

Vegetarian
24 Cafe Trang
22 Bangkok Thai
    Oasis Cafe

Wild Cards
26 Martine (Mediterranean)
25 Red Iguana (Mexican)
    Mandarin/G (Chinese)
23 Siegfried's Deli (German)
21 Cafe Madrid (Spanish)

Worth a Trip
27 Grapevine/G
    Logan
    Mariposa/P
    Deer Valley
26 Glitretind/P
    Deer Valley
    Chez Betty/P
    Park City
    Center Cafe/G
    Moab

Top 20 Decor Ranking

29 La Caille
27 Tuscany
Log Haven
Grappa/P
26 Metropolitan
Mariposa/P
Glitretind/P
Foundry Grill/S
New Yorker Club
Chimayo/P
Sundance Tree Room/S
25 Grapevine/G
Goldener Hirsch/P
Ichiban Sushi
Baci Trattoria
24 Fresco
Spencer's
Zoom/P
Millcreek Inn
23 Martine

Outdoor

Fresco
Glitretind/P
Goldener Hirsch/P
Grapevine/G
La Caille
Log Haven
Millcreek Inn
Sundance Tree Room/S
Tuscany
Zoom/P

Romantic

Glitretind/P
Grapevine/G
Grappa/P
La Caille
Log Haven
Millcreek Inn
Sundance Tree Room/S
Tuscany

Rooms

Baci Trattoria
Foundry Grill/S
Garden Wall/G
Grappa/P
La Caille
Log Haven
Mariposa/P
Metropolitan
New Yorker Club
Tuscany

Views

Glitretind/P
Goldener Hirsch/P
La Caille
Log Haven
Sundance Tree Room/S
Yurt, The/C

Top 20 Service Ranking

26 Grapevine/G
25 New Yorker Club
Mariposa/P
Glitretind/P
Fresco
Primo
24 Martine
Goldener Hirsch/P
23 Chez Betty/P
Log Haven
Metropolitan
La Caille
Spencer's
Riverhorse Cafe/P
Rino's
22 Grappa/P
Yurt, The/C
Sundance Tree Room/S
Foundry Grill/S
Seafood Buffet/P

Best Buys

20 Top Bangs For The Buck

This list reflects the best dining values in our *Survey*. It is produced by dividing the cost of a meal into the combined ratings for food, decor and service.

1. Tony Caputo's
2. Cannella's
3. Siegfried's Deli
4. Brick Oven/G
5. Lion House Pantry
6. Bluebird Cafe/G
7. Red Iguana
8. Cucina
9. Rio Grande Cafe
10. Cafe Trang
11. Mandarin/G
12. Red Rock Brewing Co.
13. Red Butte Cafe
14. Wasatch Brew Pub/P
15. Maddox Ranch House/G
16. Kyoto
17. Dodo
18. Magleby's/G
19. Oasis Cafe
20. Rodizio Grill

Alphabetical Directory of Utah Restaurants

Salt Lake City & Environs

TOP 3 FOOD RANKING

	Restaurant	Cuisine Type
27	Fresco	Northern Italian
26	New Yorker Club	American/Continental
	Martine	Med./New American

F	D	S	C

Absolute!   20 | 20 | 20 | $29
52 W. 200 South (bet. Main & W. Temple Sts.), Salt Lake City, 801-359-0899
☑ "Convenient before Capitol Theatre performances", this "trendy" Downtown Scandinavian-influenced Continental with white pillars and high ceilings has a "lovely" ambiance; a few find the fare "unimaginative", but the staff "tries hard."

Al Forno's Ristorante   22 | 16 | 19 | $22
239 S. 500 East, Salt Lake City, 801-359-6040
☑ Surveyors agree that this "small" Downtown venue's "dependable", "down-home" Italian cuisine easily makes up for its "out-of-the-way location" near a Laundromat.

Baci Trattoria   22 | 25 | 22 | $27
134 W. Pierpont Ave. (W. Temple St., bet. 200 & 300 South), Salt Lake City, 801-328-1500
☑ Vaulted ceilings and stained-glass murals typify the "artsy" decor at this Downtown Italian, which is a "fun place to be seen and have a good meal" before the theater or a hoops game; while dissenters acknowledge the menu's "wide variety", they find the preparations "inconsistent."

Bambara 🆂   – | – | – | M
Hotel Monaco, 202 S. Main St. (W. 200 South), Salt Lake City, 801-363-5454
Set in a trendy Downtown hotel, this hip New American newcomer boasts a smashing art deco interior and up-to-the-minute cuisine; since it's across the street from the Capitol Theatre, check out the pre-performance menu.

Bangkok Thai 🆂   22 | 18 | 19 | $22
Foothill Village, 1400 S. Foothill Dr., 2nd fl. (2300 East & 1300 South), Salt Lake City, 801-582-8424
☑ "Thank God for real ethnic food in the land of white bread" declares the "loyal clientele" of this Eastside Thai serving "excellent vegetarian" dishes and "some off-the-wall items" for those pining for a "change from typical Asian fare."

Big City Soup   ▽ 24 | 15 | 21 | $15
235 S. 400 West (Pierpont Ave.), Salt Lake City, 801-333-7687
■ This spare, utilitarian room adjacent to a proposed Downtown real estate development boasts a "great concept" – "gourmet soups served with little goodies" like mini–Tabasco bottles, mints and enormous hunks of chewy bread; devotees find the selection "exciting", but warn that management may "need to add a few things to the menu" to survive a climb in temperature.

Cafe Madrid   21 | 14 | 20 | $23
2080 E. 3900 South, Holladay, 801-273-0837
■ The "owners and staff ensure a great evening" at this "surprisingly good surburban outpost" for "reasonably priced", "authentic" "Spanish home cooking" (the "best tapas in SLC", "spectacular interpretations of traditional recipes"); it's "definitely worth the drive" to Holladay, but call ahead to order paella (24-hour advance notice) and to reserve a table in the "small but cozy" space.

Cafe Rio   – | – | – | I
6985 S. Park Ctr. Dr. (S. 1300 East), Salt Lake City, 801-562-4431
"A cut above" fresh Mexican grill (with branches in Provo and St. George) that draws crowds of students and families; most agree "it's worth the extra dollar or two" for hefty burritos made with homemade tortillas or for lighter fare such as a chicken or beef fajita salad topped with spicy tomatillo ranch dressing – "my friends love this place."

Cafe Trang S   24 | 13 | 19 | $15
818 S. Main St. (bet. 800 & 900 South), Salt Lake City, 801-539-1638
Cottonwood Mall, 4835 S. Highland Dr., Holladay, 801-278-8889
☑ This long-standing Downtown Vietnamese features "outstanding noodles and soups" and a "large vegetarian menu"; aesthetes assert that the decor is "dingy", but "cheap eats" keep the crowds coming; N.B. the new suburban branch in Holladay is unrated.

Caffé Molise   24 | 19 | 21 | $23
55 W. 100 South (bet. Main & W. Temple Sts.), Salt Lake City, 801-364-8833
■ A "godsend" "before and after Downtown activities" drawing bravos for its "nice patio", "great" Italian cuisine from a seasonal menu and "excellent service."

Cannella's   21 | 16 | 20 | $11
204 E. 500 South, Salt Lake City, 801-355-8518
☑ This cozy, appealingly remodeled Downtown tribute to the red, white and green appeals to lunchtime Gen Xers who want "consistently good edibles and friendly service" on the cheap; cheerleaders who yell "we want more homemade Italian" wish they were "open for dinner" more often (Thursday and Friday nights only).

Capitol Cafe S
23 | 23 | 22 | $29

54 W. 200 South (bet. Main & W. Temple Sts.), Salt Lake City,
801-532-7000
☑ A "favorite lunch spot" for folks on "expense accounts",
and "convenient" for Capitol Theatre ticketholders too, this
Downtown Continental-Eclectic bistro offers "flashes of
brilliance" from the kitchen and "stylish" decor reminiscent
"of NYC"; nonetheless, some express concern about a
"recent chef change" and find it "overpriced."

Cucina S
23 | 21 | 16 | $15

1026 E. Second Ave. (bet. Q & R Sts.), Salt Lake City,
801-322-3055
■ "Fabulous" "creative salads" and sandwiches that
attain "perfection" are the stars at this Avenues deli; while
the setting has a "relaxed" "European feel", a few prefer
takeout "for faculty staff meetings" or "an evening hike."

Dodo Restaurant S
22 | 17 | 20 | $19

1321 S. 2100 East, Salt Lake City, 801-583-5055
☑ Recently relocated to Eastside digs is this New American
former favorite of the Downtown lunch set; it still has some
of the "best soup and sandwich combos" around ("try the
turkey"), a "to-die-for" cookie-dough pie and a "great patio",
but now also boasts a more modern, art-filled dining room.

Em's
▽ 25 | 17 | 23 | $20

250 S. 400 West (Pierpont Ave.), Salt Lake City, 801-596-0566
☑ Crisp linens and simple lines define this pastel-colored,
lunch-only Eclectic in a converted warehouse just west of
Downtown; since it's run by "caring professionals" who
turn out "excellent" seasonal cuisine, it's not surprising
that everyone "hopes it makes it."

Five Alls Restaurant
23 | 21 | 20 | $30

1458 S. Foothill Dr. (2300 East), Salt Lake City, 801-582-1400
☑ Shields and swords on the walls contribute to the "Old
English" ambiance at this "longtime superior" Eastside
seafooder-steakhouse where patrons "feel pampered"
over traditional "full-course meals for one price"; cutting-
edge diners find it "dark" and "stuffy" and think the menu
"should join the '90s" (or better yet, the 21st century), but
it's hard to argue with 31 years of "anniversary celebrations."

FRESCO ITALIAN CAFE S
27 | 24 | 25 | $34

1513 S. 1500 East (bet. Emerson & Kensington Aves.),
Salt Lake City, 801-486-1300
■ Rated No.1 for Food in the *Utah Survey*, this Eastside
"perennial favorite" serves "excellent" and "delicious"
Northern Italian food in a "lovely setting" (an adjoining
bookstore adds ambiance); "dining on the patio [and
garden] in summer is preferred", but in any season it's
"an intimate pleasure that never disappoints", thus
"reservations are a must."

Ginza
| 23 | 17 | 18 | $22 |

209 W. 200 South, Salt Lake City, 801-322-2224

☑ Sashay over to the sushi bar and enjoy "first-rate" raw fish at this "bright", "hip" Downtown Japanese convenient to the theater or symphony hall; its popular cooked items include the usual suspects (sukiyaki, teriyaki, udon) as well as a few less familiar items, such as Ginza *nabe* (a seafood, vegetable and tofu chowder).

Ichiban Sushi & Japanese Cuisine 🅂
| 26 | 25 | 20 | $29 |

336 S. 400 East, Salt Lake City, 801-532-7522

■ Even if "you think you don't like sushi, the Japanese-trained female chef will teach you" to ("try the Funky Charlie"– just one of the "very creative" "killer" offerings here); while regulars "thank God" this longtime Park City spot moved to a spiffed-up Downtown SLC location in an old church, several respondents specify that you take a "seat at the sushi bar" because service can be "slow" elsewhere in the room.

Kyoto 🅂
| 22 | 20 | 21 | $20 |

1080 E. 1300 South, Salt Lake City, 801-487-3525

■ "You always see the owner talking to customers" at this "friendly" Eastside Japanese that's so "dependable", it's even safe to "send your parents"; moreover, while the cuisine may "transport" you to the land of the rising sun, the portions are strictly "Utahian" ("how can people eat this much?"); N.B. a limited selection of sushi is served Friday–Sunday night only.

LA CAILLE 🅂
| 20 | 29 | 23 | $53 |

Little Cottonwood Canyon, 9565 S. Wasatch Blvd. (3500 East), Sandy, 801-942-1751

☑ "One of the most beautiful restaurants in the country" and voted No.1 for Decor in the *Utah Survey* is this "idyllic" Sandy French "château retreat"; while critics carp about the sky-high tab ("you pay for the ambiance and bosoms" – i.e. the waitresses' "revealing period uniforms"), atmosphere addicts insist this "exceptional special-occasion place" deserves attention, while business types tout it as "great for the expense-account crowd."

Le Parisien 🅂
| 20 | 17 | 20 | $22 |

417 S. 300 East, Salt Lake City, 801-364-5223

☑ Despite its Gallic name and dishes such as "yummy Dover sole" and onion soup, this "longtime backup for a great dinner" Downtown actually serves Italian as well as French fare; though the peaceful atmosphere appeals to the senior set ("my kind of place, I can hear"), younger diners think the setting is starting to "show its age."

Lion House Pantry   20 | 20 | 18 | $13
63 E. South Temple St. (bet. Main & State Sts.), Salt Lake City, 801-363-5466

🔳 A "homey" Downtown place "to meet Aunt Mildred" that's "known for its history" as part of Brigham Young's original pioneer settlement and still dishes out "Mormon, Utah", pantry-style grub, which means rolls, "good mashed potatoes", the "best value on prime rib" and lots of pies; sophisticates call the victuals "bland" and "boring", but concede that "kids love the selections"; N.B. unusual hours mean you should call ahead.

Little America Dining Room 🆂   22 | 20 | 21 | $22
Little America Hotel, 500 S. Main St., Salt Lake City, 801-363-6781

🔳 "Still doing a great job" says the loyal "gray"-haired clientele of this Downtown American dining room drawing praise for its "rustic charm", fireplace, "best buffet in town" and Sunday brunch; whippersnappers call it "basic hotel food", but ratings side with their elders, who know better.

LOG HAVEN ◖🆂   25 | 27 | 23 | $37
6451 E. 3800 South (Wasatch Blvd., 4 mi. up Millcreek Canyon), Salt Lake City, 801-272-8255

■ Its "unsurpassed", "spectacular" "mountain setting" – a "revived" lodge nestled in thick pines and wildflowers accented by a lily-pad pond – is "worth the trip" up Millcreek Canyon; almost as highly rated is the "innovative" and "delicious" American-Eclectic cuisine; all in all, for "celebrations and romance", it's one of the "best dining experiences" in the area.

MARKET STREET BROILER 🆂   24 | 21 | 21 | $25
260 S. 1300 East, Salt Lake City, 801-583-8808

■ Set in a "historic old firehouse" near the University campus, this Eastside seafooder from Gastronomy Inc. serves "huge portions" of "simply prepared", "excellent" fish, which is guaranteed to be fresh based on "the sheer volume of business" alone; finatics sit on the patio for "summertime casual pleasure", at the counter when eating solo and in the main dining room when "hosting out-of-town guests."

Market Street Grill 🆂   25 | 22 | 22 | $25
54 Market St. (Main St., bet. 300 & 400 South), Salt Lake City, 801-322-4668

■ Seafooder and "Salt Lake mainstay" – anchor of the successful Gastronomy Inc. group – that some label a Downtown "neighborhood wonder" for "fresh fish", the "best blackened chicken plate (and it's not even on the menu)" and "good breakfasts"; yes, it's "noisy", "but that's the fun" and locals rely on it for "regular dinners out."

Market Street Oyster Bar ⑤   24 22 21 $29
54 Market St. (W. Temple St., bet. 300 & 400 South),
Salt Lake City, 801-531-6044
■ The "club side of the Market Street Grill", this Downtown
seafood bar is a "fun place to hang" and draws votes for
the "best raw oysters in Utah"; "great people-watching
by the windows" is another plus.

MARTINE   26 23 24 $30
22 E. 100 South (bet. Main & State Sts.), Salt Lake City,
801-363-9328
■ "Off to a strong start and getting better" say boosters
of this Med–New American yearling that's "just what SLC
needs – a hip, delicious place Downtown"; "imaginative",
"unusual dishes" include "fun-to-graze-on tapas", while
the "pub menu at lunch is a proven winner"; devotees
declare that they do "things right" and are "consistent
enough to recommend" anytime.

METROPOLITAN   26 26 23 $51
173 W. Broadway (300 South, bet. 200 West & W. Temple St.),
Salt Lake City, 801-364-3472
◩ "Someone brought an urbane New York bistro and
dropped it" in Downtown Salt Lake say admirers of this
"beautiful" New American with "exquisite food" (albeit
presented in "dime-sized portions") and an "unforgettable
tasting menu"; the less sophisticated snipe that the
"pretentious" atmosphere means you "must wear black –
or sit behind the fern", and wallet-watchers warn that the
tab may require "a second mortgage", but sybarites simply
shrug that the "big splurge is worth it."

Michelangelo Ristorante   24 12 20 $30
Hyland Plaza Mall, 2156 S. Highland Dr., Salt Lake City,
801-466-0961
■ For a "lasting fix" of "authentic" Tuscan fare, folks flock to
this Eastside basement Italian, where you'll "wish the room
were prettier" ("the Sistine chapel it ain't") but appreciate
the "personable" staff straight from the old country and the
"fresh", "fantastic" food, including breads, pastas and
desserts that are all made on the premises.

Millcreek Inn   23 24 21 $34
Millcreek Canyon Rd. (3 mi. up 3800 South), Salt Lake City,
801-278-7927
■ "Perfect summer patio dining" can be had with a visit to
this Eastside Continental-American nestled in a "romantic",
"woodsy" setting about three miles up Millcreek Canyon;
atmospherics aside, the chef (a CIA graduate) earns kudos
for his "finely presented", "flavorful" food.

NEW YORKER CLUB | 26 | 26 | 25 | $43 |
60 W. Market St. (Main St., bet. 300 & 400 South),
Salt Lake City, 801-363-0166
■ Longtime "chef Will Pliler is a master" at this Downtown
American-Continental that, despite a basement setting,
remains Gastronomy Inc.'s "ritzy" "crown jewel"; the
"consistently excellent food", "gracious service" and
"great wine list" set a "benchmark for excellence" and
draw the "pretty people", making it a place "to go to
close a deal" or when "you're feeling romantic."

Oasis Cafe S | 21 | 22 | 19 | $21 |
151 S. 500 East, Salt Lake City, 801-322-0404
■ A "refreshing" "lunchtime alternative to burgers", this
"casual" Downtown International-Vegetarian oasis adjacent
to a bookstore draws everyone from "New-Agey" types
to curious "meat eaters" with the "best weekend brunch"
out on the patio; N.B. some seafood is served as well.

Primo | 24 | 20 | 25 | $31 |
2350 E. Front Union Blvd. (7000 South), Holladay, 801-947-0024
■ What some call "the best restaurant in the valley" is a
"consistently excellent" Continental-Italian offering the
"quiet atmosphere of European restaurants" and "fresh",
"simple food dressed up"; what's more, it's "friendly" and
"not crowded" – all in all, a "nice place to go for special
occasions", despite its Holladay strip mall setting.

Red Butte Cafe S | 21 | 19 | 18 | $18 |
Foothill Village Shopping Ctr., 1414 Foothill Dr. (S. 2300 East),
Salt Lake City, 801-581-9498
■ Suburban SLC Southwestern in a hectic mini-mall that
earns a "local treasure" tag from fans who praise the
"lively", "interesting" fare like "well-prepared" pastas
and "good cakes and pies" from the in-house bakery ; it's
"loud", but since it's convenient to the University, "casual"
and reasonably priced, it qualifies as a "great date spot."

Red Iguana, The S | 25 | 13 | 18 | $14 |
736 W. North Temple St., Salt Lake City, 801-322-1489
■ This Downtown "gastronomic gem" may be a "hole-in-
the-wall", but many surveyors say it's the "best Mexican"
in SLC, serving "great moles" and other "authentic" entrees
that always draw a crowd; despite the "kitschy", "very
east LA decor" and "lack of seating", devotees decree
that it's the place for "killer food" – "I crave it in my sleep."

Red Rock Brewing Company S | 21 | 20 | 20 | $18 |
254 S. 200 West, Salt Lake City, 801-521-7446
■ Conveniently located in a converted warehouse near the
Delta Center, this popular brewpub is a "trendy place to
go with friends" "after Jazz games" to munch on "above-
average" salads, sandwiches, pizzas and American entrees
and sip one of the homemade beers or sodas.

Rino's S | 23 | 23 | 23 | $26 |
2302 E. Parleys Way (2100 South), Salt Lake City,
801-484-0901
■ Impressed surveyors note that chef Rino "uses veggies
and herbs he grows himself" at this "old-fashioned"
Eastside Italian with "very fresh" dishes, "attentive waiters"
and an art-filled dining room sporting "cozy booths"; P.S.
try to snag a table on the grapevine-laden patio.

Rio Grande Cafe S | 21 | 19 | 19 | $15 |
270 S. Rio Grande St. (450 West), Salt Lake City,
801-364-3302
◪ It may be "everyone's second-favorite Mexican", but
some question how the "lady mannequin hanging in the
giant taco shell" works with the "historic setting" in a
late-1800s train depot (adjacent to the new Gateway retail
development); fans chat up "the biggest and best cheese
enchiladas" and "quick, friendly service", but hotheads
scream "add some spice to something!"

Rivers Effortless Dining S | – | – | – | M |
6405 S. 3000 East, Holladay, 801-733-6600
Situated near the base of Big Cottonwood Canyon is this
mammoth Contemporary American newcomer featuring a
fountain-filled, river rock–accented interior, house-brewed
beers and a big menu with something for everyone; long
hours, easy freeway access and a warm staff should help
it pay down what must be a whopping mortgage.

Rodizio Grill S | 21 | 19 | 21 | $21 |
459 Trolley Sq. (700 East & 600 South), Salt Lake City,
801-220-0500
◪ A "carnivore's delight", this "fun" Trolley Square Brazilian-
style steakhouse draws "long lines" for its endless quantities
(AYCE) of 12 types of meat, as well as its American salad bar;
naysayers pan the "noisy", "three-ring circus" atmosphere.

Sakura Sushi | 25 | 13 | 18 | $22 |
6196 S. Highland Dr. (2300 East), Holladay,
801-277-3741
■ "Sushi for the adventurous" (at least for Utah) provides
an "oasis of freshness" at this unprepossessing Japanese in
the middle of a busy Holladay intersection; with "reasonable
prices" and high quality, it can "get crowded", so insiders
go early on weekends.

Siegfried's Delicatessen ⌿ | 23 | 12 | 16 | $11 |
69 W. 300 South (Broadway), Salt Lake City,
801-355-3891
■ With the closing of Marianne's, this Downtown deli/
restaurant now offers the "closest thing" to "real" German
food in town, and is a "great deal for a lunch" of Wiener
schnitzel and sauerkraut finished off by a piece of Black
Forest cake; lunch only.

SPENCER'S FOR STEAKS & CHOPS S
| 26 | 24 | 23 | $39 |

Doubletree Hotel, 255 S. West Temple St. (bet. 200 & 300 South), Salt Lake City, 801-238-4748

■ "Classic", "very upscale" Downtown American whose "good, high-end steaks" are dubbed the "best Chicago beef in the region"; a "cigar-friendly bar" and a "great selection of martinis" make this "unique for Utah" addition a "place where you can remember what being on an expense account was like."

Tony Caputo's Market & Deli S
| 23 | 19 | 21 | $12 |

308 W. 300 South, Salt Lake City, 801-531-8669

■ "Salt Lake needed this" "time travel back to Brooklyn", an olive oil–savvy Downtown Italian deli with "aromas that cannot be resisted", a staff of "happy people who want you to eat well" and lots of "fresh bread", cheese and cold cuts for a "quick", "yummy sandwich."

TUSCANY S
| 23 | 27 | 22 | $33 |

2832 E. 6200 South (Holladay Blvd.), Holladay, 801-277-9919

■ "Impress out-of-towners with SLC chic" at this "favorite" Holladay destination, which showcases "romantic Northern Italian dining" with a "luxurious setting" and "great atmosphere" in which to savor "innovative cuisine", accompanied by a "wonderful wine list" and served by an "impeccable" staff; "though it's quite big", it's a "gorgeous" "place to be seen", so prepare for a "mob scene."

Ski Areas

COTTONWOOD CANYONS

Shallow Shaft 🅂   25 | 17 | 20 | $31
Alta Ski Resort, Little Cottonwood Canyon Rd., Alta, 801-742-2177
■ "Not shallow, and you don't get shafted" proclaim fans of this "cozy" Little Cottonwood pre–Mark Miller SW offering "hearty, flavorful dinners"along with "great views" of Alta ski runs; "the best wine list in the Canyon" is another draw.

Yurt, The 🅂   25 | 23 | 22 | $45
Solitude Ski Resort, Big Cottonwood Canyon, 801-534-1400
■ For "yummy food and exercise too", cross-country ski or snowshoe to the Yurt to sample "winter wonderland dining" on "excellent" American cuisine; those who "return yearly" advise it "should be experienced by anyone who likes good food in an unusual setting"; N.B. open during ski season only.

PARK CITY/DEER VALLEY/HEBER

TOP 3 FOOD RANKING

Restaurant	Cuisine Type
27 Mariposa	New American
26 Glitretind	New American
Chez Betty	American/Continental

Blind Dog Grill ▽   23 | 22 | 22 | $35
Prospector Sq., 1781 Sidewinder Dr. (Gold Dust Ln.), Park City, 435-655-0800
■ "Outstanding crab cakes" earn raves for this "new and wonderful" Park City Regional American offering the "best ever" East Coast–style seafood and "great specials"; the "excellent service" earns more barks of approval.

CHEZ BETTY 🅂   26 | 20 | 23 | $41
Copperbottom Inn, 1637 Short Line Rd. (Deer Valley Dr.), Park City, 435-649-8181
■ It may take a map to locate this Continental-American in a Park City hotel, but its "excellent" food and "polished service" offset the "gloomy decor"; fans find it the "most pleasing and least pretentious" eating experience in Utah.

Chimayo Southwestern Grill 🅂   24 | 26 | 21 | $38
368 Main St. (4th St.), Park City, 435-649-6222
☑ An "interesting interior" backed up by "spirited food and service" makes this "awesome" SW on Main Street "popular with visitors and locals" alike; a few whine it's "way too expensive for what you get", but folks – this is Park City!

GLITRETIND RESTAURANT S   26 | 26 | 25 | $45
Stein Eriksen Lodge, 7700 Stein Way (Royal St.), Deer Valley, 435-645-6455

■ At this "sophisticated but not stuffy" New American in Deer Valley, the "outstanding" "food is as gorgeous as the mountain setting" ("what a view!"); sure, it's "pricey" and the "place to see and be seen" ("look for Stein [Eriksen] wanna-bes"), but "it's great for a special occasion."

Goldener Hirsch S   24 | 25 | 24 | $42
Goldener Hirsch Inn, 7570 Royal St. E., Deer Valley, 435-649-7770

■ A "ritzy atmosphere" with "fine European decor" and ravishing mountain views, plus "consistent" cuisine and an "excellent wine list" help this Deer Valley Continental-American claim high ratings, not to mention what some call "the best clientele in Utah."

GRAPPA ITALIAN RESTAURANT S   24 | 27 | 22 | $46
151 Main St. (Swede Alley), Park City, 435-645-0636

☑ The "place to be in Park City", particularly for a "romantic supper date", is the take on this "atmospheric" Italian filled with "beautiful people"; while opponents opine it's "overpriced" and "overrated", most maintain "freshness reigns" here, making for an "unforgettable meal" that's "worth every penny."

Juniper at Snowed Inn S   23 | 23 | 21 | $39
3770 N. Hwy. 224, Park City, 435-647-3311

■ Surveyors who've discovered this cozy, "charming" Park City New American nook nestled in a historic lodge hail it as a "hidden pleasure", especially for the "excellent" "chef's choice" dinners; a very few find it "too pricey", but toss in an attractive setting, a "superior wine list" and "good service", and it's a "no-brainer choice" for most.

MARIPOSA, THE S   27 | 26 | 25 | $47
Silver Lake Lodge, Deer Valley Resort, 7600 Royal St., Deer Valley, 435-645-6715

■ This "great retreat" at Deer Valley Resort's Silver Lake Lodge is a "class act" offering "imaginative" New American dishes that are "as good as it gets", an "elegant" ambiance and "amazing service"; it may "flatten your credit card", but that doesn't stop a "clientele of beautiful people" from packing the place; N.B. open December–mid-April.

Mediterraneo S   22 | 20 | 19 | $32
628 Park Ave. (Hebrew Ave.), Park City, 435-647-0030

■ A "true Mediterranean" at the base of Park City's Main Street offering "wonderful outdoor dining in summer" and sun-drenched coziness to cast off chills in winter; for some it's good "for wine and tapas before dinner", but others settle in for main meals of paella, bouillabaisse and such.

Riverhorse Cafe S 24 | 23 | 23 | $41
540 Main St., Park City, 435-649-3536

◪ There's controversy over this New American on Main serving what supporters call "consistently well-prepared food" that's "expensive but worth every penny"; foes gripe it "has seen better days" and now hawks "more attitude than food" to its "noisy" "yuppie" clientele, but defenders, backed up by high ratings, swear it's still "outstanding."

Seafood Buffet 25 | 21 | 22 | $44
Snow Park Lodge, Deer Valley, 435-645-6632

◪ "Don't eat that day – you'll want to load up" advise vets of the "awesome" buffet at this rustic ski lodge at the base of Deer Valley; critics warn "quantity's not always quality", but fans count on "superb sautéed fish", a warm fire and smashing mountain views; N.B. ski season only.

Simon's at the Homestead S 20 | 22 | 20 | $29
The Homestead Resort, 700 N. Homestead Dr. (Hwy. 40), Midway, 435-654-1102

◪ The "lovely dining room" and "beautiful view of the lake" and mountains make this Heber Valley Regional American in a historic Swiss resort "delightful" for a "romantic evening"; though a few find it somewhat "blah", most applaud the "very good", seasonally changing Western menu and agree it's "worth the drive" – you could even opt to stay over and take a soak in the mineral baths.

Snake Creek Grill S – | – | – | M
650 W. 100 South, Heber City, 435-654-2133

Chef Barbara Hill (ex Riverhorse Cafe and Zoom) goes out on her own with this Regional American on the main road to Midway; expect several comfy, flower-and-photograph-filled rooms and a moderately priced menu that includes intensely seasoned fish and poultry dishes as well as neighborhood-pleasing basics like mac 'n' cheese.

350 Main S 23 | 20 | 21 | $33
350 Main St., Park City, 435-649-3140

◼ One of only two fresh oyster bars in the state is found in this Park City New American–seafooder in a historic building on Main; folks "can't say enough about the excellent food" (from bistro-style classics to innovative creations like ancho chile shrimp cakes) and drop more pearls for the "great decor"; even those "not much for seafood are impressed."

Wasatch Brew Pub S 18 | 19 | 19 | $18
250 Main St., Park City, 435-649-0900

◪ Although "it's better to go here for the beer than for the food or service", this Park City brewpub's "young clientele" is generally satisfied with the "average" bar fare and focuses more on the chance to "sample lots of good beer" in a "fun atmosphere" with deck dining and a convenient top of Main location.

Zoom ⑤　　　　　　　　23 ⏐ 24 ⏐ 20 ⏐ $32
660 Main St. (Heber Ave.), Park City, 435-649-9108

☑ "A fancy restaurant that has the guts to offer macaroni and cheese deserves praise" claim adherents of this Robert Redford–owned Park City American offering "supergenerous portions" of "interesting", "classy" "diner food" in a "wonderful rustic setting"; though a few growl it's "too trendy" (conversely, some are disappointed to find "no movie stars"), most give it a thumbs-up – it's "almost as good as the Sundance restaurants."

SUNDANCE

FOUNDRY GRILL ⑤　　　　　23 ⏐ 26 ⏐ 22 ⏐ $28
Sundance Resort, Rural Rte. #3 (North Fork, Provo Canyon), Sundance, 801-223-4220

■ Robert Redford's Regional American at the Sundance Resort earns Oscar nominations from surveyors for its "delicious food" ("wonderful brunch"), "attentive staff" and mountain-bound, streamside setting complete with "rustic", ranch-elegant furnishings and patio; while it may not rival Deer Valley for amenities, it is open year-round and has a nearby screening room that's popular when the ski lifts park for the season.

Sundance Tree Room ⑤　　　　25 ⏐ 26 ⏐ 22 ⏐ $40
Sundance Resort, Six mi. up Provo Canyon (North Fork Canyon Rd.), Sundance, 801-223-4200

■ There's a "gorgeous mountain ski resort setting" for this Sundance American with a Western accent that's co-owned by Robert Redford; offering "very creative food" and a "comfortable", "inviting" ambiance, it's the "best of the best" ("only the tree is dead – the rest is a true treasure").

Greater Utah

TOP 3 FOOD RANKING

	Restaurant	Cuisine Type
27	Grapevine	Continental
26	Center Cafe	International
25	Mandarin	Chinese

F	D	S	C

Bluebird Cafe 17 | 19 | 19 | $13
19 N. Main St. (Center St.), Logan, 435-752-3155
■ Boasting nearly 90 years on Logan's Main Street, this "classic Americana cafe" "brings back memories" with its "working soda fountain" and "even better homemade chocolates"; though a few go just to "admire the period fountain", most chirp happily about the "good" Traditional American fare at this "step back in time" in Cache Valley.

Brick Oven 21 | 20 | 20 | $14
111 E. 800 North, Provo, 801-374-8800
◩ "A great place for nostalgia" say devotees of this "fun" '50s BYU pizza/pasta joint in Provo that draws crowds with its "outstanding" pies; it may be "nothing spectacular", but "standard family fare in a family town" is still a winning formula after more than 40 years.

Cafe Diablo S ∇ 25 | 19 | 21 | $27
599 W. Main St. (N. Center St.), Torrey, 435-425-3070
■ The "best place to get a real meal after a week of camping" out is at this "oasis in the desert" in remote Torrey, near Capitol Reef National Park; the few who know about this Southwesterner run by a husband-and-wife team feel that its "hot and spicy" food and homemade desserts are "surprisingly good for a small town."

Cafe Rio – | – | – | I
2250 N. University Pkwy. (W. 2230 North), Provo, 801-375-5133
245 N. Red Cliffs Dr. (bet. N. Mall Dr. & N. 1950 East), St. George, 435-688-0606 S
See review under Salt Lake City & Environs.

Center Cafe S 26 | 19 | 22 | $29
92 E. Center St. (Main St.), Moab, 435-259-4295
■ A "classy" "jewel in the desert", this "creative" International in red rock country serves what fans call "the best food in a town known for rocks and dirt"; although some "can't believe this restaurant resides in Moab" and wonder if it's "too expensive for such an outdoorsy town", others warn the "small seating area" fills up quickly at what's easily "Southern Utah's best."

Garden Wall Restaurant, The   ▽ | 22 | 25 | 24 | $28 |
Thanksgiving Point, 2095 N. West Frontage Rd. (I-15, exit 287), Lehi, 801-768-4990

■ Set in a family-focused Lehi complex offering shopping and golf is this "beautiful" European garden–inspired Regional American with handpainted dining rooms; fans tout the "unusual ways of fixing wonderful food" and appreciate the "good prices" but note the "no drinks" (including coffee) policy – owners hope the 32 flavors of hot chocolate compensate.

GRAPEVINE, THE | 27 | 25 | 26 | $33 |
129 N. 100 East (bet. 100 & 200 North), Logan, 435-752-1977

■ "An unbelievable find" tucked away in a historic Victorian home surrounded by gardens filled with lavender and grapevines, this chef-owned-and-operated Logan "gem" steals the crowds from Cache Valley and beyond "given no competition" when it comes to the "always excellent" Continental cuisine; limited hours (dinner only, Wednesday–Saturday) mean it's "almost always full."

Maddox Ranch House | 22 | 16 | 20 | $18 |
1900 S. Hwy. 89, Perry, 435-723-8545

☑ The "great beef", "fried chicken and fresh pies are heavenly" at this long-standing "family favorite" serving Traditional American "comfort food" in a "great old home" where "they treat you like friends"; although it's so popular it gets "way too crowded" (and some find it "like an assembly line"), most agree it's "worth the drive" to Perry (on I-15 North) for "quintessential hometown food and hospitality"; N.B. no alcohol.

Magleby's | 21 | 20 | 21 | $21 |
1675 N. 200 West (University Pkwy.), Provo, 801-374-6249

■ "Holding its own after several years on top" in a "unique" park-like setting is this Provo seafooder-steakhouse with some Cajun accents; it earns the most kudos for its "fresh, homestyle cooking" ("wonderful breadsticks"), but "everything is good – food, service and atmosphere"; for a few boosters, it's an all-time "favorite."

MANDARIN | 25 | 19 | 20 | $18 |
348 E. 900 North, Bountiful, 801-298-2406

■ A trip to Bountiful could bring you to the "best Chinese ever", an "always crowded" stalwart with a "vast" menu, "consistently fresh, flavorful, quality ingredients" and "fab-o food"; some insiders advise "order the Peking duck 48 hours ahead – it's the only way to get a reservation" and avoid the "much too long wait."

Indexes to Utah Restaurants

Special Features and Appeals

CUISINES*

American (New)
Bambara
Dodo
Glitretind/P
Juniper at Snowed Inn/P
Log Haven
Mariposa/P
Martine
Metropolitan
Riverhorse Cafe/P
Rivers Effortless Dining
350 Main/P
Yurt/C
Zoom/P

American (Regional)
Blind Dog Grill/P
Chimayo/P
Foundry Grill/S
Garden Wall/G
Lion House Pantry
Shallow Shaft/C
Simon's at the Homestead/P
Snake Creek Grill/P
Sundance Tree Room/S
Zoom/P

American (Traditional)
Bluebird Cafe/G
Chez Betty/P
Goldener Hirsch/P
Little America
Maddox Ranch Hse./G
Millcreek Inn
New Yorker
Red Rock Brewing
Spencer's
Wasatch Brew Pub/P
Yurt/C (seasonal)
Zoom/P

Brazilian
Rodizio Grill

Chinese
Mandarin/G

Continental
Absolute!
Capitol Cafe
Chez Betty/P
Goldener Hirsch/P
Grapevine/G
Millcreek Inn
New Yorker
Primo

Delis/Sandwich Shops
Cucina
Siegfried's Deli
Tony Caputo's

Eclectic/International
Bambara
Capitol Cafe
Center Cafe/G
Em's
Log Haven
Oasis Cafe

French
La Caille
Le Parisien

German
Siegfried's Deli

Italian
(N=Northern; S=Southern;
N&S=Includes both)
Al Forno's (N&S)
Baci Trattoria (N)
Brick Oven/G (N&S)
Caffé Molise (N&S)
Cannella's (S)
Fresco (N)
Grappa/P (N&S)
Le Parisien (N&S)
Michelangelo (N)
Primo (N)
Rino's (N&S)
Tony Caputo's (N&S)
Tuscany (N)

---

* All restaurants are in Salt Lake City & Environs unless otherwise
noted (C=Cottonwood Canyons; G=Greater Utah; P=Park City/Deer
Valley/Heber area; S=Sundance).

Japanese
Ginza
Ichiban Sushi
Kyoto
Sakura Sushi

Mediterranean
Martine
Mediterraneo/P

Mexican/Tex-Mex
Cafe Rio
Cafe Rio/G
Red Iguana
Rio Grande Cafe

Pizza
Brick Oven/G

Seafood
Five Alls
Magleby's/G
Market St. Broiler
Market St. Grill
Market St. Oyster Bar
Oasis Cafe
Seafood Buffet/P
350 Main/P

Soups
Big City Soup

Southwestern
Cafe Diablo/G
Chimayo/P
Red Butte Cafe
Shallow Shaft/C

Spanish
Cafe Madrid

Steakhouses
Five Alls
Maddox Ranch Hse./G
Magleby's/G
Rodizio Grill
Spencer's

Thai
Bangkok Thai

Vegetarian
(Most Chinese, Indian and
Thai restaurants)
Bangkok Thai
Cafe Trang
Oasis Cafe

Vietnamese
Cafe Trang

LOCATIONS

SALT LAKE CITY & ENVIRONS

Downtown
Absolute!
Al Forno's
Baci Trattoria
Bambara
Big City Soup
Cafe Trang
Caffé Molise
Cannella's
Capitol Cafe
Em's
Ginza
Ichiban Sushi
Le Parisien
Lion House Pantry
Little America
Market St. Grill
Market St. Oyster Bar
Martine
Metropolitan
New Yorker
Oasis Cafe
Red Iguana
Red Rock Brewing
Rio Grande Cafe
Rodizio Grill
Siegfried's Deli
Spencer's
Tony Caputo's

Eastside
Bangkok Thai
Cucina
Dodo
Five Alls
Fresco
Kyoto
Market St. Broiler
Michelangelo
Millcreek Inn
Red Butte Cafe
Rino's

Holladay/Murray/ Midvale
Cafe Madrid
Cafe Rio
Cafe Trang
Log Haven
Primo
Rivers Effortless Dining
Sakura Sushi
Tuscany

Sandy/West Jordan/ West Valley
La Caille

COTTONWOOD CANYONS

Shallow Shaft

Yurt

PARK CITY/DEER VALLEY/HEBER

Blind Dog Grill
Chez Betty
Chimayo
Glitretind
Goldener Hirsch
Grappa
Juniper at Snowed Inn
Mariposa

Mediterraneo
Riverhorse Cafe
Seafood Buffet
Simon's at the Homestead
Snake Creek Grill
350 Main
Wasatch Brew Pub
Zoom

SUNDANCE

Foundry Grill

Sundance Tree Room

GREATER UTAH

Davis County
Mandarin

Northern Utah
Bluebird Cafe
Grapevine
Maddox Ranch Hse.

Southern Utah
Cafe Diablo
Cafe Rio
Center Cafe

Utah County
Brick Oven
Cafe Rio
Garden Wall
Magleby's

SPECIAL FEATURES AND APPEALS*

Business Dining
Absolute!
Al Forno's
Bangkok Thai
Caffé Molise
Capitol Cafe
Chez Betty/P
Chimayo/P
Dodo
Em's
Fresco
Garden Wall/G
Glitretind/P
Goldener Hirsch/P
Grapevine/G
Grappa/P
Juniper at Snowed Inn/P
Le Parisien
Lion House Pantry
Little America
Log Haven
Maddox Ranch Hse./G
Magleby's/G
Mandarin/G
Mariposa/P
Market St. Broiler
Market St. Grill
Market St. Oyster Bar
Martine
Metropolitan
New Yorker
Oasis Cafe
Primo
Red Butte Cafe
Red Rock Brewing
Rio Grande Cafe
Riverhorse Cafe/P
Rodizio Grill
Spencer's
350 Main/P
Tuscany
Zoom/P

Caters
(Best of many)
Absolute!
Al Forno's
Bangkok Thai

Big City Soup
Blind Dog Grill/P
Brick Oven/G
Cafe Diablo/G
Cafe Trang
Caffé Molise
Cannella's
Capitol Cafe
Chimayo/P
Cucina
Em's
Foundry Grill/S
Fresco
Garden Wall/G
Grappa/P
Juniper at Snowed Inn/P
La Caille
Little America
Oasis Cafe
Rino's
Rio Grande Cafe
Shallow Shaft/C
Siegfried's Deli
Tony Caputo's
Wasatch Brew Pub/P

Dancing/Entertainment
(Check days, times and
performers for entertainment;
D=dancing; best of many)
Glitretind/P (jazz)
Goldener Hirsch/P (varies)
Grapevine/G (Violin)
Metropolitan (jazz)
Riverhorse Cafe/P (varies)

Delivers*/Takeout
(Nearly all Asians, coffee
shops, delis, diners and
pasta/pizzerias deliver or do
takeout; here are some
interesting possibilities;
D=delivery, T=takeout; *call
to check range and charges,
if any)
Absolute! (T)
Al Forno's (T)
Big City Soup (T)

---

* All restaurants are in Salt Lake City & Environs unless otherwise
  noted (C=Cottonwood Canyons; G=Greater Utah; P=Park City/Deer
  Valley/Heber area; S=Sundance).

Blind Dog Grill/P (T)
Brick Oven/G (D,T)
Cafe Diablo/G (D,T)
Cafe Madrid (T)
Capitol Cafe (T)
Center Cafe/G (T)
Dodo (T)
Foundry Grill/S (D,T)
Fresco (T)
Garden Wall/G (T)
Le Parisien (D,T)
Lion House Pantry (T)
Little America (T)
Maddox Ranch Hse./G (T)
Market St. Broiler (T)
Martine (T)
Oasis Cafe (T)
Primo (T)
Red Butte Cafe (T)
Red Rock Brewing (T)
Rino's (T)
Rodizio Grill (T)
Shallow Shaft/C (T)
Siegfried's Deli (T)
Spencer's (T)
Sundance Tree Room/S (T)
350 Main/P (T)
Tony Caputo's (T)
Tuscany (T)
Wasatch Brew Pub/P (T)

Dessert/Ice Cream

Garden Wall/G
Lion House Pantry
Market St. Broiler
Market St. Grill
Market St. Oyster Bar
New Yorker
Tuscany
Zoom/P

Dining Alone

(Other than hotels, coffee
shops, sushi bars and places
with counter service)
Big City Soup
Caffé Molise
Martine
New Yorker
Rivers Effortless Dining

Fireplaces

Cafe Diablo/G
Cafe Trang

Chez Betty/P
Chimayo/P
Dodo
Five Alls
Foundry Grill/S
Fresco
Garden Wall/G
Glitretind/P
Goldener Hirsch/P
Grappa/P
Juniper at Snowed Inn/P
Log Haven
Mariposa/P
Metropolitan
Sundance Tree Room/S
350 Main/P
Tuscany
Wasatch Brew Pub/P

Historic Interest

(Year opened; *building)
1860 Lion House Pantry*
1890 Rio Grande Cafe*
1900 Market St. Broiler*
1900 Market St. Grill*
1900 Market St. Oyster Bar*
1900 New Yorker*
1910 Chimayo/P*
1914 Bluebird Cafe/G
1930 Log Haven*

Hotel Dining

Alta Ski Resort
    Shallow Shaft/C
Copperbottom Inn
    Chez Betty/P
Doubletree Hotel
    Spencer's
Goldener Hirsch Inn
    Goldener Hirsch/P
Homestead Resort
    Simon's at the Homestead/P
Hotel Monaco
    Bambara
Little America Hotel
    Little America
Silver Lake Lodge
    Mariposa/P
Snow Park Lodge
    Seafood Buffet/P
Solitude Ski Resort
    Yurt/C
Stein Eriksen Lodge
    Glitretind/P

Sundance Resort
  Foundry Grill/S
  Sundance Tree Room/S

"In" Places
Big City Soup
Brick Oven/G
Cafe Diablo/G
Cafe Madrid
Capitol Cafe
Center Cafe/G
Chez Betty/P
Chimayo/P
Cucina
Glitretind/P
Mariposa/P
Market St. Broiler
Market St. Oyster Bar
Metropolitan
New Yorker
Red Butte Cafe
Red Iguana
Red Rock Brewing
Rivers Effortless Dining
Rodizio Grill
Tony Caputo's
Tuscany
Zoom/P

Noteworthy Newcomers (9)
Bambara
Big City Soup
Blind Dog Grill/P
Cafe Rio
Em's
Martine
Rivers Effortless Dining
Rodizio Grill
Snake Creek Grill/P

Noteworthy Closings (7)
Barking Frog Grille
Bill & Nada's Cafe
Hungry i
Il Sansovino
L'Hermitage
Pomodoro
Roundhouse at Solitude

Offbeat
Big City Soup
Center Cafe/G
Market St. Oyster Bar
Red Iguana

Snake Creek Grill/P
Yurt/C

Outdoor Dining
(G=garden; P=patio;
S=sidewalk; T=terrace;
W=waterside; best of many)
Absolute! (S)
Baci Trattoria (P)
Bangkok Thai (P)
Blind Dog Grill/P (P)
Cafe Diablo/G (G,P)
Cafe Madrid (P)
Caffé Molise (G,P)
Cannella's (S)
Capitol Cafe (S)
Chez Betty/P (P)
Cucina (P)
Dodo (P)
Em's (S)
Foundry Grill/S (P,W)
Fresco (G,P,T)
Glitretind/P (T)
Goldener Hirsch/P (P)
Grapevine/G (G,P)
Grappa/P (G,P,T)
Juniper at Snowed Inn/P (T)
La Caille (G,P)
Log Haven (G,P,W)
Market St. Broiler (P)
Millcreek Inn (P)
Oasis Cafe (G,P)
Red Butte Cafe (P)
Rino's (P)
Rio Grande Cafe (G,P)
Riverhorse Cafe/P (P)
Simon's at the Homestead/P
  (G,P)
Sundance Tree Room/S (P)
350 Main/P (P)
Tony Caputo's (S)
Tuscany (G,P,T)
Zoom/P (G,P)

Outstanding Views
Foundry Grill/S
Glitretind/P
Goldener Hirsch/P
La Caille
Log Haven
Seafood Buffet/P
Shallow Shaft/C
Simon's at the Homestead/P
Sundance Tree Room/S

Tuscany
Yurt/C

Parking/Valet

(L=parking lot;
V=valet parking;
*=validated parking)
Absolute!*
Bambara (V)
Caffé Molise*
Capitol Cafe*
Foundry Grill/S (V)
Glitretind/P (V)
Goldener Hirsch/P (L)*
Kyoto (L)
Lion House Pantry*
Log Haven (V)
Market St. Grill (L,V)*
Market St. Oyster Bar (L,V)
Martine*
Metropolitan*
New Yorker (L,V)*
Red Rock Brewing (L)*
Spencer's (V)*
Tuscany (L,V)

Parties & Private Rooms

(Any nightclub or restaurant
charges less at off-times;
* indicates private rooms
available; best of many)
Absolute!
Baci Trattoria
Bambara
Bangkok Thai
Blind Dog Grill/P
Brick Oven/G
Cafe Diablo/G
Cafe Trang
Capitol Cafe
Center Cafe/G
Chimayo/P
Em's
Foundry Grill/S
Garden Wall/G*
Grappa/P
Juniper at Snowed Inn/P
Le Parisien*
Lion House Pantry
Little America
Log Haven
Maddox Ranch Hse./G
Magleby's/G*
Mandarin/G

Mariposa/P
Metropolitan
Millcreek Inn
New Yorker
Red Butte Cafe
Red Rock Brewing
Rino's
Riverhorse Cafe/P
Rodizio Grill
Shallow Shaft/C
Spencer's
Sundance Tree Room/S*
350 Main/P
Tony Caputo's
Tuscany
Wasatch Brew Pub/P
Zoom/P

People-Watching

Chimayo/P
Foundry Grill/S
Glitretind/P
Goldener Hirsch/P
Grappa/P
Mariposa/P
Market St. Broiler
Market St. Grill
Market St. Oyster Bar
Martine
Metropolitan
New Yorker
Red Butte Cafe
Red Rock Brewing
Riverhorse Cafe/P
Rivers Effortless Dining
Spencer's
350 Main/P
Tony Caputo's
Tuscany
Zoom/P

Power Scenes

Baci Trattoria
Bambara
Market St. Grill
Metropolitan
New Yorker
Spencer's

Pre-Theater/
Early Bird Menus

(Call to check prices,
days and times)
Absolute!
Baci Trattoria

Bambara
Brick Oven/G
Capitol Cafe
Mandarin/G
Market St. Broiler
Market St. Grill
Market St. Oyster Bar
Martine
New Yorker
Rivers Effortless Dining
Spencer's

Post-Theater/
Late Supper Menus
(Call to check prices,
days and times)
Absolute!
Bambara
Brick Oven/G
Capitol Cafe
Little America
Market St. Oyster Bar
New Yorker
Red Rock Brewing
Spencer's
350 Main/P

Prix Fixe Menus
(Call to check prices,
days and times)
Brick Oven/G
Foundry Grill/S
Garden Wall/G
Mariposa/P
Martine
Metropolitan
New Yorker

Quiet Conversation
Cafe Diablo/G
Cafe Madrid
Caffé Molise
Capitol Cafe
Em's
Fresco
Glitretind/P
Juniper at Snowed Inn/P
Le Parisien
Little America
Log Haven
Martine
Michelangelo
Millcreek Inn
Oasis Cafe

Primo
Rino's
Rivers Effortless Dining
Tuscany
Zoom/P

Reservations Essential
Bambara
Capitol Cafe
Chez Betty/P
Five Alls
Fresco
Garden Wall/G
Grapevine/G
La Caille
Log Haven
Mariposa/P
Metropolitan
New Yorker
Sundance Tree Room/S
Tuscany
Yurt/C

Romantic Spots
Cafe Madrid
Five Alls
Fresco
Glitretind/P
Goldener Hirsch/P
Grapevine/G
Grappa/P
La Caille
Log Haven
Mariposa/P
Metropolitan
Millcreek Inn
New Yorker
Primo
Riverhorse Cafe/P
Shallow Shaft/C
Simon's at the Homestead/P
Spencer's
Sundance Tree Room/S
Tuscany

Saturday – Best Bets
(B=brunch; L=lunch;
best of many)
Al Forno's (L)
Baci Trattoria (L)
Bangkok Thai (L)
Brick Oven/G (L)
Cafe Trang (L)

Capitol Cafe (B,L)
Cucina (L)
Dodo (L)
Foundry Grill/S (L)
Garden Wall/G (B,L)
Glitretind/P (L)
Goldener Hirsch/P (L)
Kyoto (L)
Le Parisien (L)
Lion House Pantry (L)
Maddox Ranch Hse./G (L)
Magleby's/G (L)
Market St. Broiler (L)
Market St. Grill (L)
Oasis Cafe (B,L)
Red Iguana (L)
Red Rock Brewing (B,L)
Rivers Effortless Dining (B,L)
Rodizio Grill (L)
Siegfried's Deli (L)
Wasatch Brew Pub/P (L)
Zoom/P (L)

Sunday – Best Bets
(B=brunch; L=lunch;
D=dinner; plus all hotels
and most Asians)
Capitol Cafe (B,L,D)
Cucina (B,L)
Dodo (B)
Market St. Broiler (L,D)
Market St. Grill (B,D)
Market St. Oyster Bar (B,D)
Oasis Cafe (B,L,D)
Red Butte Cafe (B,D)
Red Iguana (L,D)
Red Rock Brewing (B,L,D)
Rivers Effortless Dining (B,L,D)
Rodizio Grill (L,D)
Tuscany (B,D)
Wasatch Brew Pub/P (L,D)
Zoom/P (L,D)

Senior Appeal
Le Parisien
Lion House Pantry
Little America
Maddox Ranch Hse./G
Mandarin/G
Rodizio Grill

Singles Scenes
Brick Oven/G
Cafe Diablo/G

Center Cafe/G
Martine
Red Butte Cafe
Red Rock Brewing
Rivers Effortless Dining
Rodizio Grill
Tony Caputo's
Wasatch Brew Pub/P
Zoom/P

Sleepers
(Good to excellent food,
but little known)
Big City Soup
Cafe Diablo/G
Center Cafe/G
Em's
Foundry Grill/S
Garden Wall/G
Grapevine/G
Juniper at Snowed Inn/P
Magleby's/G
Primo
Sakura Sushi
Shallow Shaft/C

Teenagers & Other Youthful Spirits
Brick Oven/G
Cafe Diablo/G
Cafe Rio
Cafe Rio/G
Red Butte Cafe
Rivers Effortless Dining
Rodizio Grill

Visitors on Expense Accounts
Bambara
Chez Betty/P
Fresco
Grapevine/G
Grappa/P
La Caille
Log Haven
Mariposa/P
Metropolitan
New Yorker
Spencer's
350 Main/P
Tuscany

Wheelchair Access

(Most places now have
wheelchair access; call in
advance to check)

Winning Wine Lists

Chez Betty/P
Chimayo/P
Fresco
Glitretind/P
Grapevine/G
Grappa/P
Juniper at Snowed Inn/P
Log Haven
Mariposa/P
Metropolitan
New Yorker
Spencer's
Tuscany

Worth a Trip

Bountiful
    Mandarin/G
Deer Valley
    Glitretind/P
    Goldener Hirsch/P
    Mariposa/P
Heber
    Snake Creek Grill/P
Logan
    Grapevine/G
Moab
    Center Cafe/G
Park City
    Chez Betty/P
    Chimayo/P
    Grappa/P
    Riverhorse Cafe/P
    Zoom/P

Perry
    Maddox Ranch Hse./G
Sundance
    Foundry Grill/S
    Sundance Tree Room/S
Torrey
    Cafe Diablo/G

Young Children

(Besides the normal fast-food
places; * indicates children's
menu available)
Baci Trattoria*
Bambara*
Bluebird Cafe/G
Brick Oven/G
Cafe Diablo/G*
Cafe Rio/G
Chimayo/P*
Foundry Grill/S*
Garden Wall/G*
Glitretind/P*
Goldener Hirsch/P*
Grappa/P*
Kyoto*
Little America*
Maddox Ranch Hse./G*
Market St. Broiler*
Red Butte Cafe*
Rodizio Grill
Shallow Shaft/C*
Simon's at the Homestead/P
Sundance Tree Room/S*
350 Main/P*

ALPHABETICAL PAGE INDEX

NOTES

NOTES

NOTES

NOTES

Wine Vintage Chart 1985-1998

This chart is designed to help you select wine to go with your meal. It is based on the same 0 to 30 scale used throughout this *Survey*. The ratings (prepared by our friend **Howard Stravitz**, a law professor at the University of South Carolina) reflect both the quality of the vintage and the wine's readiness for present consumption. Thus, if a wine is not fully mature or is over the hill, its rating has been reduced. We do not include 1987, 1991 or 1993 vintages because, with the exception of cabernets, '91 Northern Rhônes and '93 red Burgundies and Southern Rhônes, those vintages are not especially recommended.

	'85	'86	'88	'89	'90	'92	'94	'95	'96	'97	'98
WHITES											
French:											
Alsace	25	20	23	28	28	24	28	26	24	25	24
Burgundy	24	25	19	27	22	23	22	27	28	25	24
Loire Valley	–	–	–	26	25	18	22	24	26	23	22
Champagne	28	25	24	26	28	–	–	24	26	24	–
Sauternes	22	28	29	25	26	–	18	22	23	24	–
California:											
Chardonnay	–	–	–	–	–	24	22	26	22	26	26
REDS											
French:											
Bordeaux	26	27	25	28	29	18	24	25	24	23	23
Burgundy	24	–	23	27	29	23	23	25	26	24	24
Rhône	26	20	26	28	27	15	23	24	22	24	26
Beaujolais	–	–	–	–	–	–	21	24	22	24	23
California:											
Cab./Merlot	26	26	–	21	28	26	27	25	24	25	26
Zinfandel	–	–	–	–	–	21	23	21	22	24	25
Italian:											
Tuscany	27	–	24	–	26	–	–	25	19	28	25
Piedmont	25	–	25	27	27	–	–	23	25	28	25

Bargain sippers take note: Some wines are reliable year in, year out, and are reasonably priced as well. They include: Alsatian Pinot Blancs, Côtes du Rhône, Muscadet, Bardolino, Valpolicella and inexpensive Spanish Rioja and California Zinfandel and are best bought in the most recent vintages.